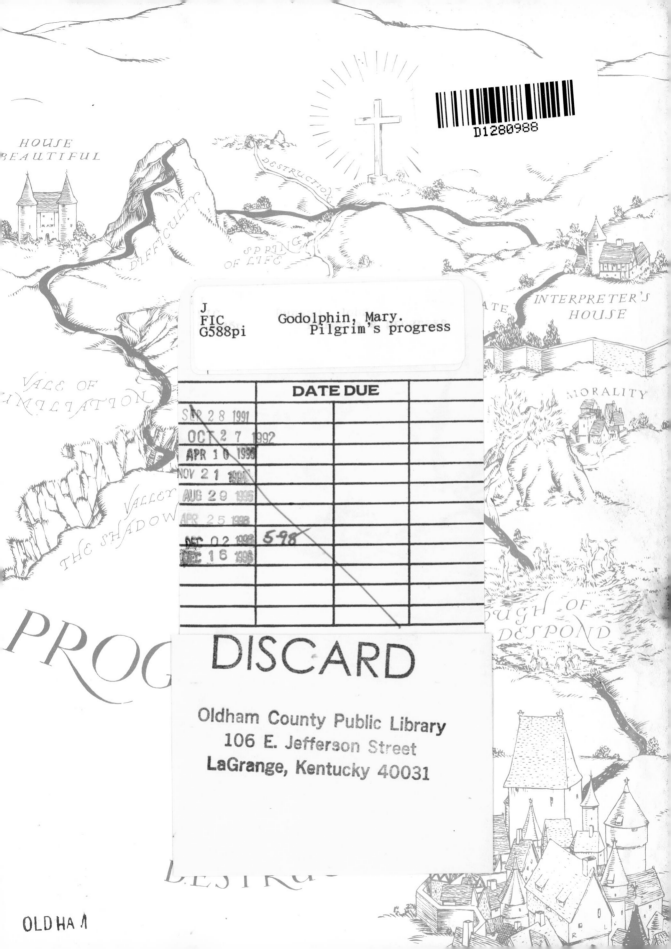

PILGRIM'S PROGRESS

PILGRIM'S

By JOHN BUNYAN

RETOLD AND SHORTENED FOR MODERN READERS, BY MARY GODOLPHIN · 1884

D01914

PROGRESS

Drawings by ROBERT LAWSON

PUBLISHED BY J.B. LIPPINCOTT
COMPANY · PHILADELPHIA · NEW YORK

FOREWORD

On my wife's third Christmas her colored "Mammy" presented her with a book—*The Pilgrim's Progress.* It was an abridged and simplified edition of John Bunyan's great old classic, published by McLoughlin Brothers, New York, in 1884 and illustrated with lurid and rather depressing colored lithographs.

The simplification and abridgment were done by one Mary Godolphin, somewhat surprisingly credited on the title page as the "Author" of *Robinson Crusoe, Evenings at Home* and *The Swiss Family Robinson.* Nowhere is poor Bunyan even mentioned.

This tattered and dog-eared little volume has long held an honored place on our bookshelves and it was there that Helen Dean Fish discovered it one evening last spring. Struck by the shortness and simplicity of the text she decided that here was the basis for a new "picture-book" edition, she to rewrite it and I to illustrate it. On further study, however, it became apparent that Mary Godolphin, despite her apparent lack of modesty, had done an almost perfect job and it was decided to use her text exactly as it stood.

Without omitting any of the better known incidents, she has yet managed to shorten Bunyan's extremely wordy and repetitious story to less than one-fifth its original length. With this excess wordage removed, Pilgrim really makes Progress and his journey to the Promised Land becomes a fast moving story of adventure, with giants, dragons and excitements galore.

For the many children who, finding Bunyan's original wordiness a veritable Slough of Despond, have, like Pliable, given up and gone home, this volume ought to prove a pleasanter way of becoming acquainted with one of the most widely read stories ever written.

To their parents I might quote from Mary Godolphin's rather quaint "Author's Preface": "There is a large class of persons who do not begin to acquire the art of reading until somewhat late in life, and it is for such that I think a book of this Character is peculiarly applicable."

As for the illustrations, I have tried more than anything else to make the characters living and real, with fairly accurate costumes and surroundings of Bunyan's time. If a certain element of caricature or humor appears, seemingly out of place in a book so essentially religious, I can only say that it is there because I think John Bunyan would have wanted it that way. His message is forcefully and crudely expressed and when he gave characters such name as Mr. Worldly Wiseman or Mr. Stubborn or Mr. Live-loose, I think he wanted them to look worldly-wise or stubborn or loose-lived—very. When he describes the beauties and delights of the Promised Land I think he would have wanted them pictured as beautifully as possible and this I have sincerely tried to do.

I feel the deepest gratitude to Helen Dean Fish, whose enthusiasm has made this edition possible, and the Frederick A. Stokes Company, who have allowed me complete freedom in every detail of the illustration and arrangement of the book, and to McLoughlin Brothers, who very graciously permitted use of the text. Such co-operation has made six months of hard labor a most joyful period.

ROBERT LAWSON

Rabbit Hill
March, 1939.

ILLUSTRATIONS

PART ONE

As I went through the wild waste of this world, I came to
a place where there was a den, and I lay down in it to sleep.
While I slept, I had a dream, and lo! I saw a man whose
clothes were in rags, and he stood with his face from his own
house, with a book in his hand, and a great load on his back.
I saw him read from the leaves of a book, and as he read,
he wept and shook with fear — then he let out a loud cry,
and said, "What shall I do to save my soul?"

So in this plight he went home, and as long as he could he

held his peace, that his wife and babes should not see his grief. But at length he told them his mind, and thus he spoke: "Oh, my dear wife, and you, my babes, I, your dear friend, am full of woe, for a load lies hard on me; and more than this, I have been told that our town will be burnt with fire, in which I, you my wife, and you my sweet babes, shall be lost, if means be not found to save us."

This sad tale struck all who heard him with awe, not that they thought what he said to them was true, but that they had fears that some weight must be on his mind; so, as night now drew near, they were in hopes that sleep might soothe his brain, and with all haste they got him to bed.

When the morn broke, they sought to know how he did? He told them, "Worse and worse", and he set to talk once more in the same strain as he had done; but they took no heed of it. By and by, to drive off his fit, they spoke harsh words to him; at times they would laugh, at times they would chide, and then set him at nought. So he went to his room to pray for them, as well as to nurse his own grief. He would go, too, in the woods to read and muse, and thus for some weeks he spent his time.

Now I saw, in my dream, that one day as he took his walk in the fields with his book in his hand, he gave a groan, for he felt as if a cloud were on his soul, and he burst out as he was wont to do, and said, "Who will save me?" I saw, too, that he gave wild looks this way and that, as if he would rush off; yet he stood still, for he could not tell which way to go. At last a man, whose name was Evangelist, came up to him and said, "Why dost thou weep?"

He said, "Sir, I see by this book in my hand that I am to die, and that then God will judge me. Now I dread to die."

Evangelist asked: "Why do you fear to die, since this life is fraught with woe?"

The man said, "I fear lest a hard doom should wait me, and that this load on my back will make me sink down, till at last, I shall find I am in Tophet."

"If this be your case," said Evangelist, "why do you stand still?"

But the man said, "I know not where to go."

Then Evangelist gave him a scroll with these words on it, *"Fly from the wrath to come."*

When the man read it he said, "Which way must I fly?"

Evangelist held out his hand to point to a gate in a wide field, and said, "Do you see the Wicket Gate?"

The man said, "No."

"Do you see that light?"

He then said, "I think I do."

"Keep that light in your eye," quoth Evangelist, "and go straight up to it; so shall you see the gate, at which, when you knock, it shall be told you what you are to do."

Then I saw in my dream that Christian — for that was his name — set off to run.

Now he had not gone far from his own door, when his wife and young ones, who saw him, gave a loud wail to beg of him to come back; but the man put his hands to his ears, and ran on with a cry of "Life! Life!" The friends of his wife, too, came out to see him run, and as he went, some were heard to mock him, some to use threats, and there were

two who set off to fetch him back by force, the names of whom were Obstinate and Pliable. Now, by this time, Christian had gone a good way off, but at last they came up to him.

Then said Christian, "Friends why are you come?"

"To bid you go back with us," said they.

"But," quoth he, "that can by no means be; you dwell in The City of Destruction, the place where I, too, was born. I know it to be so, and there you will die and sink down to a place which burns with fire; be wise, good friends, and come with me."

"What! and leave our goods, and all our kith and kin?"

"Yes," said Christian, "for that *all* which you might leave is but a grain to that which I seek, and if you will go with me and hold it firm, you shall fare as well as I; for there, where I go, you will find all you want and to spare. Come with me, and prove my words."

· 4 ·

Obstinate: "What are the things you seek, since you leave all the world to find them?"

Christian: "I seek those joys that fade not, which are laid up in a place of bliss — safe there for those who go in search of them. Read it so, if you will, in my book."

Obstinate: "Tush! Off with your book! Will you go back with us or no?"

Christian: "No, not I, for I have laid my hand to the plough."

Obstinate: "Come, friend Pliable, let us turn back and leave him; there is a troop of such fools who, when they take up with a whim by the end, are more wise in their own eyes than ten men who know how to think."

Pliable: "Nay, do not scorn him; if what the good Christian says is true, the things he looks to are of more worth than ours: my heart leans to what he says."

Obstinate: "What! more fools still! Go back, go back, and be wise."

Christian: "Nay, but do you come with your friend Pliable; there are such things to be had as those I just spoke of, and more, too. If you give no heed to me, read here in this book which comes to us from God, who could not lie."

Pliable: "Well, friend Obstinate, I think now I have come to a point; and I mean to go with this good man, and to cast my lot in with his." Then said he to Christian, "Do you know the way to the place you speak of?"

Christian: "I am told by a man whose name is Evangelist, to do my best to reach a gate that is in front of us, where I shall be told how to find the way."

So they went on side by side.

Obstinate: "And I will go back to my place; I will not be one of such vain folk."

Now I saw in my dream, that when Obstinate was gone back, Christian and Pliable set off to cross the plain, and they spoke thus as they went:

Christian: "Well, Pliable, how do you do now? I am glad you have a mind to go with me."

Pliable: "Come, friend Christian, since there are none but

we two here; tell me more of the things of which we go in search."

Christian: "I can find them in my heart, though I know not how to speak of them with my tongue; but yet, since you wish to know, this book tells us of a world that has no bounds, and a life that has no end."

Pliable: "Well said, and what else?"

Christian: "That there are crowns of light in store for us, and robes that will make us shine like the sun."

Pliable: "This, too, is good; and what else?"

Christian: "That there shall be no more care or grief; for he that owns the place shall wipe all tears from our eyes."

Pliable: "And what friends shall we find there?"

Christian: "There we shall be with all the saints, in robes so bright that our eyes will grow dim to look on them. There shall we meet those who in this world have stood out for the faith, and have been burnt on the stake, and thrown to wild beasts, for the love they bore to the Lord. They will not harm us, but will greet us with love, for they all walk in the sight of God."

Pliable: "But how shall we share all this?"

Christian: "The Lord of that land saith, if we wish to gain that world we shall be free to have it."

Pliable: "Well, my good friend, glad am I to hear of these things: come on, let us mend our pace."

Christian: "I cannot go so fast as I would, for this load on my back."

Then I saw in my dream that just as they had come to an end of this talk, they drew near to a slough that was in the midst of the plain, and as they took no heed, they both fell in. The name of the slough was Despond. Here they lay for a time in the mud; and the load that Christian had on his back made him sink all the more in the mire.

Pliable: "Ah! friend Christian, where are you now?"

Christian: "In truth, I do not know."

Then Pliable said to his friend, "Is this the bliss of which you have told me all this while? If we have such ill speed when we first set out, what may we look for 'twixt this and the end of our way?" And with that he got out of the mire on that side of the slough which was next to his own house; then off he went, and Christian saw him no more.

So Christian was left to strive in the Slough of Despond as well as he could; yet his aim was to reach that side of the slough that was next The Wicket Gate, which at last he did, but he could not get out for the load that was on his back; till I saw in my dream that a man came to him whose name was Help.

"What do you do here?" said Help.

Christian: "I was bid to go this way by Evangelist, who told me to pass up to yon gate, that I might flee from the wrath to come, and on my way to it I fell in here."

Help: "But why did you not look for the steps?"

Christian: "Fear came so hard on me that I fled the next way and fell in."

Help: "Give me your hand."

So he gave him his hand, and he drew him out, and set him on firm ground, and bade him go on his way.

Then in my dream I went to Help and said to him,

The Slough of Despond

"Sir, since this place is on the way from The City of Destruction to The Wicket Gate, how is it that no one mends this patch of ground, so that those who come by may not fall in the slough?"

Help said, "This slough is such a place as no one can mend. It is the spot to which doth run the scum and filth that wait on sin, and that is why men call it the Slough of Despond. When the man of sin wakes up to a sense of his own lost state, doubts and fears rise up in his soul, and all of them drain down and sink in this place: and it is this that makes the ground so bad. True there are good and sound steps in the midst of the slough, but at times it is hard to see them; or if they be seen, men's heads are so dull that they step on one side, and fall in the mire. But the ground is good when they have once got in at the gate."

Now I saw in my dream that by this time Pliable had gone back to his house once more, and that his friends came to see him. Some said how wise it was to come home, and some that he was a fool to have gone. Some, too, were found to mock him, who said: "Well, had I set out, I would not have been so base as to come back for a slough in the road." So Pliable was left to sneak off; but at last he got more heart, and then all were heard to turn their taunts, and laugh at poor Christian. So much for Pliable.

Now as Christian went on his way he saw a man come through the field to meet him, whose name was Mr. Worldly Wiseman, and he dwelt in the town of Carnal Policy, which was near that whence Christian came. He had heard some news of Christian; for his flight from The City of Destruction had made much noise, and was now the talk far and near. So he said, "How now, good Sir, where do you go with such a load on your back?"

Christian: "In truth, it is a load; and if you ask me where I go, I must tell you, Sir, I must go to The Wicket Gate in front of me, for there I shall be put in a way to get quit of my load."

Worldly Wiseman: "Have you not a wife and babes?"

Christian: "Yes, but with this load I do not seem to care for them as I did; and, in truth, I feel as if I had none."

Worldly Wiseman: "Will you hear me if I speak my mind to you?"

Christian: "If what you say be good, I will, for I stand much in need of help."

Worldly Wiseman: "I would urge you then, with all speed, to get rid of your load; for your mind will not be at rest till then."

Christian: "That is just what I seek to do. But there is no man in our land who can take it off me."

Worldly Wiseman: "Who bade you go this way to be rid of it?"

Christian: "One that I took to be a great and true name; his name is Evangelist."

Worldly Wiseman: "Hark to what I say: there is no worse way in the world than that which he has sent you, and that you will find if you take him for your guide. In this short time you have met with bad luck, for I see the mud of the Slough of Despond is on your coat. Hear me, for I have seen more of the world than you; in the way you go, you will meet with pain, woe, thirst, the sword, too; in a word, death! Take no heed of what Evangelist tells you."

Christian: "Why, Sir, this load on my back is worse to me than all those things which you speak of; nay, I care not what I meet with in the way, if I can but get rid of my load."

Worldly Wiseman: "How did you come by it at first?"

Christian: "Why, I read this book."

Worldly Wiseman: "Like more weak men I know, who aim at things too high for them, you have lost heart, and run in the dark at great risk, to gain you know not what."

Christian: "I know that I would gain ease for my load."

· 13 ·

Worldly Wiseman: "But why will you seek for ease thus, when I could put you in the way to gain it where there would be no risk; and the cure is at hand."

Christian: "Pray, Sir, tell me what that way is."

Worldly Wiseman: "Well, in yon town, which you can see from here — the name of which is Morality — there dwells a man whose name is Legality, a wise man, and a man of some rank, who has skill to help men off with such loads as yours from their back; I know he has done a great deal of good in that way; ay, and he has the skill to cure those who, from the loads they bear, are not quite sound in their wits. To him, as I said, you may go and get help. His house is but a mile from this place, and should he not be at home, he has a son whose name is Civility, who can do it just as well as his sire. There, I say, you may go to get rid of your load. I would not have you go back to your old home, but you can send for your wife and babes, and you will find that food there is cheap and good."

Now was Christian brought to a stand; but by and by he said, "Sir, which is my way to this good man's house?"

Worldly Wiseman: "Do you see that hill?"

Christian: "Yes, I do."

Worldly Wiseman: "By that hill you must go, and the first house you come to is his."

So Christian went out of his way to find Mr. Legality's house to seek for help.

But, lo, when he had got close up to the hill, it was so steep and high that he had fears lest it should fall on his head; so he stood still, as he knew not what to do. His load, too, was of more weight to him than when he was on the right road. Then came flames of fire out of the hill, that made him quake for fear lest he should be burnt. And now it was a great grief to him that he had lent his ear to Worldly Wiseman; and it was well that he just then saw Evangelist come to meet him; though at the sight of him he felt a deep blush creep on his face for shame. So Evangelist drew near, and when he came up to him, he said, with a sad look: "What dost thou here, Christian?"

To these words Christian knew not what to say, so he stood quite mute. Then Evangelist went on thus: "Art not thou the man that I heard cry in The City of Destruction?"

Christian: "Yes, dear Sir, I am the man."

Evangelist: "Did not I point out to thee the way to The Wicket Gate?"

Christian: "Yes, you did, Sir."

Evangelist: "How is it, then, that thou hast so soon gone out of the way?"

Christian: "When I had got out of the Slough of Despond I met a man who told me that in a town near, I might find one who could take off my load."

Evangelist: "What was he?"

Christian: "He had fair looks, and said much to me, and got me at last to yield; so I came here. But when I saw this hill, and how steep it was, I made a stand, lest it should fall on my head."

Evangelist: "What said the man to thee?"

When Evangelist had heard from Christian all that took place, he said, "Stand still a while, that I may show thee the words of God."

So Evangelist went on to read, "*Now the just shall live by faith, but if a man draw back, my soul shall have no joy in him.* Is not this the case with thee?" said he. "Hast not thou drawn back thy feet from the way of peace, to thine own cost; and dost thou not spurn the most high God?"

Then Christian fell down at his feet as dead, and said, "Woe is me! Woe is me!"

At the sight of which, Evangelist caught him by the right

hand, and said, "Faith hopes all things."

Then did Christian find some peace, and stood up.

Evangelist: "I pray thee give more heed to the things that I shall tell thee of. The Lord says, 'Strive to go in at the strait gate, the gate to which I send thee, for strait is the gate that leads to life, and few there be that find it. Why didst thou set at nought the words of God, for the sake of Mr. Worldly Wiseman? This is, in truth, the right name for such as he. The Lord hath told thee that 'he who will save his life shall lose it.' He to whom thou wast sent for ease, Legality by name, could not set thee free; no man yet has got rid of his load through him; he could but show thee the way to woe, for by the deeds of the law no man can be rid of his load. So that Mr. Worldly Wiseman and his friend Mr. Legality are false guides; and as for his son Civility, he could not help thee."

Now Christian, in great dread, sent forth a sad cry in grief that he had gone from the right way. Then he spoke once more to Evangelist in these words: "Sir, what think you? Is there hope? May I now go back, and strive to reach The Wicket Gate? I grieve that I gave ear to this man's voice; but may my sin find grace?"

Evangelist: "Thy sin is great, for thou hast gone from the way that is good, to tread in false paths, yet will the man at the gate let thee through, for he has love and good will for all men. But take heed that thou turn not to the right hand or to the left."

Then did Christian make a move to go back, and Evangelist gave him a kiss and one smile, and bade him God speed.

· 17 ·

So he went on with haste, nor did he speak on the road;
and could by no means feel safe till he was in the path which
he had left. In time, he got up to the gate. And as he saw by
the words which he read on it, that those who would knock
could go in, he gave two or three knocks, and said, "May I
go in here?"

At last there came a grave man to the gate, whose name was
Good-will, and he said, "Who is there? Whence come you,
and what would you have?"

Christian: "I come from The City of Destruction with a
load of sins on my back; but I am on my way to Mount Zion,
that I may be free from the wrath to come; and as I have been
told that my way is through this gate, I would know, Sir, if
you will let me in?"

Good-will: "With all my heart."

So he flung back the gate. But just as Christian went in,
he gave him a pull.

Then said Christian: "What means that?" Good-will
told him that a short way from this gate there was a strong
fort, of which Beelzebub was the chief, and that from thence
he and the rest that dwelt there shot darts at those that came
up to the gate, to try if they could kill them ere they got in.

Then said Christian, "I come in with joy and with fear."

So when he had gone in, the man at the gate said, "Who sent you here?"

Christian: "Evangelist bade me come and knock (as I did); and he said that you, Sir, would tell me what I must do."

Good-will: "The door is thrown back wide for you to come in, and no man can shut it."

Christian: "Now I seem to reap the good of all the risks I have met with on the way."

Good-will: "But how is it that no one comes with you?"

Christian: "None of my friends saw that there was cause of fear, as I did."

Good-will: "Did they know of your flight?"

Christian: "Yes, my wife and young ones saw me go, and I heard their cries as they ran out to try to stop me. Some of my friends, too, would have had me come home, but I put my hands to my ears, and so came on my way."

Good-will: "But did none of them come out to beg of you to go back?"

Christian: "Yes, both Obstinate and Pliable came, but when they found that I would not yield, Obstinate went home, but Pliable came with me as far as the Slough of Despond."

Good-will: "Why did he not come through it?"

When Christian told him the rest, he said, "Ah, poor man! Is a world of bliss such a small thing to him, that he did not think it worth while to run a few risks to gain it?"

"Sir," said Christian, "there is not much to choose 'twixt him and me."

Then he told Good-will how he had been led from the straight path by Mr. Worldly Wiseman.

Good-will: "Oh, did he light on you? What! He would have had you seek for ease at the hands of Mr. Legality? They are, in truth, both of them cheats. And did you take heed of what he said?"

Christian then told him all. "But now that I am come," said he, "I am more fit for death, than to stand and talk to my Lord. But oh, the joy it is to me to be here!"

Good-will: "We keep none out that knock at this gate, let them have done what they may ere they came here; for they are 'in no wise cast out.' So, good Christian, come with me, and I will teach you the way you must go. Look in front. That is the way which was laid down by Christ and the wise men of old, and it is as straight as a rule can make it."

Christian: "But is there no turn or bend by which one who knows not the road might lose his way?"

Good-will: "My friend, there are not a few that lead down to it, and these paths are wide; yet by this you may judge the right from the wrong — the right are straight and are by no means wide."

Then I saw in my dream that Christian said, "Could you not help me off with this load on my back?" for as yet he had not got rid of it. He was told: "As to your load, you must bear it till you come to the place of Deliverance, for there it will fall from your back."

Then Christian would have set off on the road; but Good-will said, "Stop a while and let me tell you that when you have gone through the gate you will see the house of Mr. Interpreter, at whose door you must knock, and he will show you good things." Then Christian took leave of his friend, who bade him God speed.

He now went on till he came to the house at the door of which he was to knock. This he did two or three times. At last one came to the door and said, "Who is there?"

Christian: "I have come to see the good man of the house."

So in a short time Mr. Interpreter came to him and said, "What would you have?"

Christian: "Sir, I am come from The City of Destruction, and am on my way to Mount Zion. I was told by the man that stands at the gate, that if I came here you would show me good things that would help me."

Then Interpreter took Christian to a room, and bade his man bring a light, and there he saw on the wall the print of one who had a grave face, whose eyes were cast up to the sky; and the best of books was in His hand, the law of truth was on His lips, and the world was at His back. He stood as if He would plead for men, and a crown of gold hung near his head.

Christian: "What does this mean?"

Interpreter: "I have shown you this print first, for this is He who is to be your sole guide when you cannot find your way to the land to which you go; so take good heed to what I have shown you, lest you meet with some who would feign to lead you right; but their way goes down to death."

Then he took him to a large room that was full of dust, for it had not been swept; and Interpreter told his man to sweep it. Now when he did so, such clouds of dust flew up, that it made Christian choke.

Then said Interpreter to a maid that stood by, "Make the floor moist that the dust may not rise." And when she had done this, it was swept with ease.

Christian: "What means this?"

Interpreter: "This room is the heart of that man who knows not the grace of God. The dust is his first sin and the vice that is in him. He that swept first is the Law, but she who made the floor moist is The Book which tells Good News to Man. Now as soon as you saw the first of these sweep, the dust did so fly that the room could not be made clean by him; this is to show you that the law as it works does not cleanse the heart from sin, but gives strength to sin, so as to rouse it up in the soul.

"Then you next saw the maid come in to lay the dust; so is sin made clean and laid low by faith in The Book."

"Now," said Christian, "let me go hence."

"Well," said Interpreter, "keep all things so in thy mind that they may be a goad in thy sides; and may faith guide thee!"

Then I saw in my dream that the high way which Christian was to tread, had a wall on each side, and the name of that wall Salvation. Up this high way did Christian run, but with great toil for the load on his back. He ran thus till he drew near to a place on which stood a cross, and at the foot of it a tomb. Just as Christian came up to the cross, his load slid from his back, close to the mouth of the tomb, where it fell in, and I saw it no more.

The Load Slid from his Back

Then was Christian glad, and said with a gay heart, "He gives me rest by his grief, and life by his death." Yet he stood still for a while, for he was struck with awe to think that the sight of the cross should thus ease him of his load. Three or four times did he look on the cross and the tomb, and the tears rose to his eyes. As he stood thus and wept, lo, three Bright Ones came to him, and one of them said, "Peace be to thee! thou hast grace from thy sins." And one came up to him to strip him of his rags and put a new robe on him, while the third set a mark on his face, and gave him a roll with a seal on it, which he bade him look on as he ran, and give it in at The Celestial Gate; and then they left him.

Christian gave three leaps for joy, and sang as he went, "Ah, what a place is this! Here did the strings crack that bound my load to me. Blest cross! Blest tomb! Nay, blest is the Lord that was put to shame for me!"

He went on thus till he came to a vale where he saw three men who were in a sound sleep, with chains on their feet. The name of one was Simple, one Sloth, and the third Presumption. As Christian saw them lie in this case, he went to wake

them, and said, "You are like those that sleep on the top of a mast, for the Dead Sea is at your feet. Wake, rise, and come with me! Trust me, and I will help you off with your chains." With that they cast their eyes up to look at him, and Simple said, "I would fain take more sleep." Sloth said, "I would still sleep"; and Presumption, "Let each man look to his own." And so they lay down to sleep once more.

Then I saw in my dream that two men leapt from the top of the wall and made great haste to come up to him. Their names were Formalist and Hypocrisy.

Christian: "Sirs, when come you, and where do you go?"

Formalist and Hypocrisy: "We were born in the land of Vainglory, and are on our way to Mount Zion for praise."

Christian: "Why came you not in at the Gate? Know you not that he that comes not in at the door, but climbs up to get in, the same is a thief?"

They told him that to go through the gate was too far around; that the best way was to make a short cut of it, and climb the wall, as they had done.

Christian: "But what will the Lord of the town to which we are bound think of it, if we go not in the way of his will?"

They told Christian that he had no need for care on that score, for long use had made it law, and they could prove that it had been so for years.

Christian: "But are you quite sure that your mode will stand a suit at law?"

"Yes," said they, "no doubt of it. And if we get in the road at all, pray what are the odds? If we are in, we are in; you are but in the way, who come in at the gate, and we too are in the way that choose to climb the wall. Is not our case as good as yours?"

Christian: "I walk by the rule of my Lord, but you walk by the rule of your own lusts. The Lord of the way will count you as thieves, and you will not be found true men in the end."

I saw then that they all went on till they came to the foot of the Hill of Difficulty, where there was a spring. There were in the same place two more ways, one on the left hand and one on the right; but the path Christian was told to take went straight up the hill, and its name is Difficulty, and he saw that the way of life lay there.

Now when Christian got as far as the Spring of Life he drank of it, and then went up the hill. But when the two men saw that it was steep and high, and that there were three ways to choose from, one of them took the path the name of which is Danger, and lost his way in a great wood, and one of them went by the road of Destruction, which led him to a wide field full of dark rocks, where he fell, and rose no more.

I then saw Christian go up the hill, where at first I could see him run, then walk, and then go on his hands and knees, so steep was it. Now half way up was a cave made by the Lord of the hill, that those who came by might rest there. So here Christian sat down, and took out the scroll and read it, till at last he fell off in a deep sleep which kept him there till it was dusk; and while he slept his scroll fell from his hand. At length a man came up to him and said, "Go to the ant, thou man of sloth, and learn of her to be wise."

At this Christian gave a start, and sped on his way, and went at a quick pace.

When he had got near to the top of the hill, two men ran up to meet him, whose names were Timorous and Mistrust, to whom Christian said, "Sirs, what ails you? You run the wrong way."

Timorous said that Zion was the hill they meant to climb, but that when they had got half way they found that they met with more and more risk, so that great fear came on them, and all they could do was to turn back.

"Yes," said Mistrust, "for just in front of us there lay two beasts of prey in our path; we knew not if they slept or not, but we thought that they would fall on us and tear our limbs."

Christian: "You rouse my fears. Where must I fly to be safe? If I go back to my own town I am sure to lose my life, but if I can get to The Celestial City, there shall I be safe. To turn back is death, to go on is fear of death, but when I come there, a life of bliss that knows no end. I will go on."

So Mistrust and Timorous ran down the hill and Christian went on his way. Yet he thought once more of what he had heard from the men, and then he felt in his cloak for his scroll, that he might read it and find some peace. He felt for it but found it not. Then was Christian in great grief, and knew not what to do for the want of that which was to be his pass to The Celestial City. At last, thought he, I slept in the cave by the side of the hill. So he fell down on his knees to pray that God would give him grace for this act; and then went back to look for the scroll. But as he went, what tongue can tell the grief of Christian's heart? "Oh, fool that I am!" said he, "to sleep in the day time; so to give way to the flesh as to use for ease that rest which the Lord of the hill had made but for the help of the soul!"

Thus then, with tears and sighs, he went back, and with much care did he look on this side and on that for his scroll. At length he came near to the cave where he had sat and slept. "How far," thought Christian, "have I gone in vain! Such was the lot of the Jews for their sin; they were sent back by the way of the Red Sea; and I am made to tread those steps with grief which I might have trod with joy, had it not been for this sleep. How far might I have been on my way by this time! I am made to tread those steps thrice which I need not to have trod but once; yea, now too I am like to be lost in the night, for the day is well nigh spent. O that I had not slept!"

Now by this time he had come to the cave once more, where for a while he sat down and wept; but at last, as he cast a sad glance at the foot of the bench, he saw his scroll, which he caught up with haste, and put in his cloak. Words are too weak to tell the joy of Christian when he had got back his scroll. He laid it up in the breast of his coat, and gave thanks to God. With what a light step did he now climb the hill! But, ere he got to the top, the sun went down on Christian and he soon saw that two wild beasts stood in his way. "Ah," thought he, "these beasts range in the night for their prey; and if they should meet with me in the dark, how should I fly from them? I see now the cause of all those fears that drove Mistrust and Timorous back."

Still Christian went on, and while he thought thus on his sad lot, he cast up his eyes and saw a great house in front of him, the name of which was Beautiful, and it stood just by the side of the high road. So he made haste and went on in the hope that he could rest there a while. The name of the man who kept the lodge was Watchful, and when he saw that Christian made a halt as if he would go back, he came out to him and said, "Is thy strength so small? Fear not the two wild beasts for they are bound by chains, and are put here to try the faith of those that have it, and to find out those that have none. Keep in the midst of the path and no harm shall come to thee."

Then I saw, in my dream, that still he went on in great dread of the wild beasts; he heard them roar, yet they did him no harm; but when he had gone by them he went on with

joy, till he came and stood in front of the lodge where Watchful dwelt.

Christian: "Sir, what house is this? May I rest here to-night?"

Watchful: "This house was built by the Lord of the Hill to give aid to those who climb up it for the good cause. Tell me, whence come you?"

Christian: "I am come from the Town of Destruction, and am on my way to Mount Zion; but the day is far spent, and I would, with your leave, pass the night here."

Watchful: "How is it you came so late? The sun is set."

Christian then told him why it was.

Watchful: "Well, I will call one that lives here, who, if she like your talk, will let you come in, for these are the rules of the house."

· 31 ·

So he rang a bell, at the sound of which there came out at the door a grave and fair maid, whose name was Discretion. When Watchful told her why Christian had come there, she said: "What is your name?"

"It is Christian," said he, "and I much wish to rest here this night, and the more so for I see this place was built by the Lord of the Hill, to screen those from harm who come to it."

So she gave him a smile, but the tears stood in her eyes; and in a short time she said, "I will call forth two or three more of our house; and then she ran to the door and brought Prudence, Piety and Charity, who met him and said, "Come in, thou blest of the Lord; this house was built by the King of the Hill for such as you." Then Christian bent down his head and went with them to the house.

Piety: "Come, good Christian, since our love prompts us to take you in to rest, let us talk with you of all that you have seen on your way."

Christian: "With a right good will, and I am glad that you should ask it of me."

Prudence: "And, first, say what is it that makes you wish so much to go to Mount Zion?"

Christian: "Why, there I hope to see Him that did die on the Cross; and there I hope to be rid of all those things that to this day grieve and vex me. There, they say, is no death; and there I shall dwell with such as love the Lord."

Charity: "Have you a wife and babes?"

Christian: "Yes, I have."

Charity: "And why did you not bring them with you?"

Christian then wept, and said, "Oh, how glad should I have been to do so! But they would not come with me, nor have me leave them."

Charity: "And did you pray to God to put it in their hearts to go with you?"

Christian: "Yes, and that with much warmth, for you may think how dear they were to me."

Thus did Christian talk with these friends till it grew dark, and then he took his rest in a large room, the name of which was Peace; and there he slept till break of day, and then he sang a hymn.

They told him that he should not leave till they had shown him all the rare things that were in the place. There were to be seen the rod of Moses, the nail with which Jael slew Sisera, the lamps with which Gideon put to flight the host of Midian, and the ox goad with which Shamgar slew his foes. And they brought out the jaw bone of an ass with which Samson did such great feats, and the sling and stone with which David slew Goliath of Gath.

Then I saw in my dream that Christian rose to take his

leave of Discretion, and of Prudence, Piety, and Charity, but they said that he must stay till the next day, that they might show him The Delectable Mountains; so they took him to the top of the house, and bade him look to the South, which he did, and lo, a great way off, he saw a rich land, full of hills, woods, vines, shrubs, and streams.

"What is the name of this land?" said Christian.

Then they told him it was Immanuel's Land. "And," they said, "it is as much meant for you, and the like of you, as this hill is; and when you reach the place, there you may see the gate of The Celestial City." Then they gave him a sword, and put on him a coat of mail, which was proof from head to foot, lest he should meet some foe in the way; and they went with him down the hill.

"Of a truth," said Christian, "it is as great a toil to come down the hill as it was to go up."

Prudence: "So it is, for it is a hard thing for a man to go down to The Vale of Humiliation, as thou dost now, and for this cause have we come with you to the foot of the hill. So, though he went with great care, yet he caught a slip or two.

Then in my dream I saw that when they got to the foot of the hill, those good friends of Christian's gave him a loaf of bread, a flask of wine, and a bunch of dry grapes; and then they left him to go on his way.

But now in this Vale of Humiliation poor Christian was hard put to it, for he had not gone far, ere he saw a foe come in the field to meet him, whose name was Apollyon. Then did Christian fear, and he cast in his mind if he would go back or stand his ground. But Christian thought that as he had no coat of mail on his back, to turn round might give Apollyon a chance to pierce it with his darts. So he stood his ground, for, thought he, "if but to save my life were all I had in view, still the best way would be to stand."

So he went on, and Apollyon met him with looks of scorn.

Apollyon: "Whence come you, and to what place are you bound?"

Christian: "I am come from The City of Destruction, which is the place of all sin, and I am on my way to Zion."

Apollyon: "By this I see you are mine, for of all that land I am the Prince. How is it, then, that you have left your king? Were it not that I have a hope that you may do me more good, I would strike you to the ground with one blow."

Christian: "I was born in your realm, it is true, but you drove us too hard, and your wage was such as no man could live on."

Apollyon: "No prince likes to lose his men, nor will I as yet lose you; so if you will come back, what my realm yields I will give you."

Christian: "But I am bound by vows to the King of Kings; and how can I, to be true, go back with you?"

Apollyon: "You have made a change it seems, from bad to worse; but why not give Him the slip, and come back to me?"

Christian: "I gave Him my faith, and swore to be true to Him; how can I go back from this?"

Apollyon: "You did the same to me, and yet I will pass by all, if you will but turn and go back."

Then when Apollyon saw that Christian was stanch to his Prince, he broke out in a great rage, and said, "I hate that

· 35 ·

Prince, and I hate His laws, and I am come out to stop you."

Christian: "Take heed what you do. I am on the King's high way to Zion."

Apollyon: "I am void of fear, and to prove that I mean what I say, here on this spot I will put thee to death." With that he threw a dart of fire at his breast, but Christian had a shield on his arm, with which he caught it. Then did Christian draw his sword, for he saw it was time to stir; and Apollyon as fast made at him, and threw darts as thick as hail; with which in spite of all that Christian could do, Apollyon gave him wounds in his head, hand and foot.

This made Christian pause in the fight for a time, but Apollyon still came on, and Christian once more took heart. They fought for half a day, till Christian, weak from his wounds, was well nigh spent in strength. When Apollyon saw this, he threw him down with great force; on which Christian's sword fell out of his hand. Then said Apollyon, "I am sure of thee now!"

But while he strove to make an end of Christian, that good man put out his hand in haste to feel for his sword and caught it. "Boast not, O Apollyon!" said he, and with that he struck him a blow which made his foe reel back as one that had had his last wound. Then Apollyon spread out his wings and fled, so that Christian for a time saw him no more.

Then there came to him a hand which held some of the leaves of the tree of life; some of them Christian took, and as soon as he had put them to his wounds, he saw them heal up.

Now near this place was the Valley of the Shadow of Death, and Christian must needs go through it to get to The Celestial City. It was a land of drought and full of pits, a land that none but such as Christian could pass through, and where no man dwelt. So that here he was worse put to it than in his fight with Apollyon, which by and by we shall see.

As he drew near the Shadow of Death, he met with two men, to whom Christian thus spoke: "To what place do you go?"

Men: "Back! Back! and we would have you do the same if you prize life and peace."

Christian: "But why?"

Men: "We went on as far as we durst."

Christian: "What then have you seen?"

Men: "Seen! Why, the Valley of the Shadow of Death; but by dint of good luck we caught sight of what lay in front of it, ere we came up. Death doth spread out his wings there. In a word it is a place full of bad men, where no law dwells."

Christian: "I see not yet, by what you have told me, but that this is my way to Zion."

Men: "Be it thy way then; we will not choose it for ours."

So they took their leave and Christian went on, but still with his drawn sword in his hand, for fear lest he should meet once more with a foe.

I saw then in my dream that so far as this vale went, there was on the right hand a deep ditch; that ditch to which the blind have led the blind as long as the world has been made. And lo, on the left hand there was a quag, in which if a man fall, he will find no firm ground for his foot to stand on. The path was not broad, and so good Christian was the more put to it. This went on for miles, and in the midst of the vale was a deep pit. One thing which I saw in my dream I must not leave out; it was this: Just as Christian had come to the mouth of the pit, one of those who dwelt in it stept up to him, and in a soft tone spoke bad things to him, and took God's name in vain, which Christian thought must have come from the man's own mind. This put him out more than all the rest had done. To think that he should take the name in vain for which he felt so deep a love, was a great grief to him. Yet there was no help for it. Then he thought he heard a voice which said, *"Though I walk through the Valley of the Shadow of Death, I will fear no harm, for thou art with me."*

The Valley of the Shadow of Death

Now as Christian went on, he found there was a rise in the road, which had been thrown up that the path might be clear to those who were bound for Zion. Up this road Christian went, and soon joined a good man whose name was Faithful.

In course of time the road they took brought them to a town, the name of which is Vanity, where there is a fair kept through the whole year, and all that is bought or sold there is vain and void of worth. There, too, are to be seen at all times games, plays, fools, apes, knaves, and rogues. Yet he that will go to The Celestial City must needs pass through this fair.

As soon as Christian and Faithful came to the town, a crowd drew round them, and some said they had lost their wits, to dress and speak as they did, and to set no store by the choice of goods for sale in Vanity Fair. When Christian spoke, his words drew from these folks fierce taunts and jeers, and soon the noise and stir grew to such a height that the chief man of the fair sent his friends to take up these two strange men, and he bade them tell him whence they came, and what they did there in such a garb. Christian and Faithful told them all; but those who sat to judge the case thought that they must be mad, or else that they had come to stir up strife at the fair; so they beat them with sticks, and put them in a cage, that they might be a sight for all the men at the fair. Then the worst sort of folk set to pelt them, out of spite, and some threw at them for mere sport; but Christian and Faithful gave good words for bad, and bore all in such a meek way, that not a few took their part. This led to blows and fights, and the blame was laid on Christian and Faithful, who were then made to toil up and down the fair in chains, till, faint with stripes, they were at length set with their feet in the stocks. But they bore their griefs and woes with joy, for they saw in them a pledge that all should be well in the end.

By and by a court sat to try them. The name of the judge was Lord Hategood; and the crime laid to their charge was that they had come to Vanity Fair to spoil its trade, and stir up strife in the town; and had won not a few men to their side, in spite of the prince of the place.

Faithful said to the Judge, "I am a man of peace, and did but wage war on Sin. As for the prince they speak of, since he is Beelzebub, I hold him in scorn."

Those who took Faithful's part were won by the force of plain truth and right in his words; but the judge said, "Let those speak who know aught of this man."

So three men, whose names were Envy, Superstition, and Pick-thank, stood forth and swore to speak the truth, and tell what they knew of Faithful. Envy said, "My lord, this man cares nought for kings or laws, but seeks to spread his own views, and to teach men what he calls faith. I heard him say but now that the ways of our town of Vanity are vile. And does he not in that speak ill of us?"

Then Superstition said, "My lord, I know not much of this man, and have no wish to know more; but of this I am sure, that he is a bad man, for he says that our creeds are vain."

Pick-thank was then bid to say what he knew, and his speech ran thus: "My lord, I have known this man for a long time, and have heard him say things that ought not to be said. He rails at our great Prince Beelzebub, and says that if all men were of his mind, our prince should no more hold sway.

More than this, he hath been heard to rail at you, my lord, who are now his judge."

Then said the judge to Faithful, "Thou base man! Hast thou heard what these good folk have said of thee?"

Faithful: "May I speak a few words in my own cause?"

Judge: "Thy just doom would be to die on the spot; still, let us hear what thou hast to say."

Faithful: "I say, then, to Mr. Envy, that all laws and modes of life in which men heed not the Word of God are full of sin. As to the charge of Mr. Superstition, I would urge that nought can save us if we do not the will of God. To Mr. Pickthank, I say that men should flee from the Prince of this town and his friends, as from the wrath to come. And so, I pray the Lord to help me."

Then the judge, to sum up the case, spoke thus: "You see this man who has made such a stir in our town. You have heard what these good men have said of him, which he owns to be true. It rests now with you to save his life or hang him."

The twelve men who had Faithful's life in their hands spoke in a low tone thus:

"Out of the world with him," said Mr. No-good

"This man is full of schisms," said Mr. Blindman.

"I hate the mere look of him," said Mr. Malice.

"From the first I could not bear him," said Mr. Love-ease.

"Nor I, for he would be sure to blame my ways," said Mr. Live-loose.

"Hang him, hang him," said Mr. Heady.

"He is a rogue," said Mr. Liar.

"A low wretch!"
said Mr. High-mind.

"I long to crush him,"
said Mr. Enmity.

"Let us kill him, that
he may be out of the
way," said Mr. Hate-light.

"Death is too good for
him," said Mr. Cruelty.

Then said Mr. Implacable: "Not to gain all the world would
I make peace with him, so let us doom him to death."

And so they did, and in a short time he
was led back to the place from whence he came, there to be
put to the worst death that could be thought of; for the
scourge, the sword and the stake brought Faithful to his end.

Now I saw that there stood near the crowd a strange car with two bright steeds, which as soon as his foes had slain him, took Faithful up through the clouds straight to The Celestial City, with the sound of the harp and lute.

As for Christian, for this time he got free; and there came to join him one Hopeful, who did so from what he had heard and seen of Christian and Faithful. Thus, while one lost his life for the truth, a new man rose from his death, to tread the same way with Christian. And Hopeful said there were more men of the fair who would take their time, and then come too.

By and by their way lay just on the bank of a pure stream, from which they drank. On each side of it were green trees that bore fruit, and in a field through which it ran they lay down to sleep. When they woke up they sat for a while in the shade of the boughs. Thus they went on for three or four days, and to pass the time they sang:

"He that can tell
 What sweet fresh fruit, yea leaves these trees do yield,
 Will soon sell all, that he may buy this field."

Now on the left hand of the road was By-Path Meadow, a fair green field with a path through it, and a stile. "Come, good Hopeful," said Christian, "let us walk on the grass."

Hopeful: "But what if this path should lead us wrong?"

Christian: "How can it? Look, doth it not go by the side of the way?"

So they set off through the field. But they had not gone far when they saw in front of them a man. Vain-confidence by name, who told them that the path led to The Celestial Gate. So the man went first; but lo, the night came on, and it grew

· 46 ·

so dark, that they lost sight of their guide, who, as he did not see the path in front of him, fell in a deep pit, and was heard of no more.

"Where are we now?" said Hopeful.

Then was Christian mute, as he thought he had led his friend out of the way. And now light was seen to flash from the sky, and rain came down in streams.

Hopeful (with a groan): "Oh, that I had kept on my way!"

Christian: "Who could have thought that this path should lead us wrong?"

Hopeful: "I had my fears from the first, and so gave you a hint."

Christian: "Good friend, I grieve that I have brought you out of the right path."

Hopeful: "Say no more; no doubt it is for our good."

Christian: "We must not stand thus; let us try to go back."

Hopeful: "But, good Christian, let me go first."

Then they heard a voice say: "Set thine heart to the high way, the way thou hast been; turn once more." But by this time the stream was deep from the rain that fell, and to go back did not seem safe; yet they went back, though it was so dark and the stream ran so high that once or twice it was like to drown them. Nor could they, with all their skill, get back that night. So they found a screen from the rain, and there they slept till break of day.

Now, not far from the place where they lay was Doubting Castle, the lord of which was Giant Despair; and it was on his ground that they now slept. There Giant Despair found them, and with a gruff voice he bade them wake. "Whence are you?" said he; "and what brought you here?" They told him that they had lost the path. Then said Giant Despair: "You have no right to force your way in here; the ground on which you lie is mine."

They had not much to say, as they knew that they were in fault. So Giant Despair drove them on, and put them in a dark and foul cell in a strong hold. Here they were kept for three days, and they had no light nor food, nor a drop to drink all that time, and no one to ask them how they did. Now Giant Despair had a wife, whose name was Diffidence, and he told her what he had done. Then said he: "What will be the best way to treat them?" "Beat them well," said Diffidence. So when he rose he took a stout stick from a crab tree, and went down to the cell where poor Christian and Hopeful lay, and beat them as if they had been dogs, so that they could not turn on the floor; and they spent all that day in sighs and tears.

The next day, he came once more, and found them sore from the stripes, and said that since there was no chance for them to be let out of the cell, their best way would be to put an end to their own lives. "For why should you wish to live," said he, "with all this woe?" But they told him they did hope he would let them go. With that he sprang up with a fierce look, and no doubt would have made an end of them, but that he fell in a fit for a time, and lost the use of his hand; so he drew back, and left them to think of what he had said.

Christian: "Friend, what shall we do? The life that we now lead is worse than death. For my part I know not which is best, to live thus, or to die out of hand, as I feel that the

The Giant Despair

grave would be less sad to me than this cell. Shall we let Giant Despair rule us?"

Hopeful: "In good truth our case is a sad one, and to die would be more sweet to me than to live here; yet let us bear in mind that the Lord of that land to which we go hath said: *Thou shalt not kill.* And by this act we kill our souls as well. My friend Christian, you talk of ease in the grave, but can a man go to bliss who takes his own life? All the law is not in the hands of Giant Despair. Who knows but that God, who made the world, may cause him to die, or lose the use of his limbs as he did at first. I have made up my mind to pluck up the heart of a man, and to try to get out of this strait. Fool that I was, not to do so when first he came to the cell. But let us not put an end to our own lives, for a good time may come yet."

By these words did Hopeful change the tone of Christian's mind.

Well, at night the Giant went down to the cell to see if life was still in them, and in good truth that life was in them was all that could be said, for from their wounds and want of food they did no more than just breathe. When Giant Despair found they were not dead, he fell in a great rage, and said that it should be worse with them than if they had not been born. At this they shook with fear, and Christian fell down in a swoon; but when he came to, Hopeful said, "My friend, call to mind how strong in faith you have been till now. Say, could Apollyon hurt you, or all that you heard or saw, or felt in the Valley of the Shadow of Death? Look at the fears, the griefs, the woes that you have gone through. And now to be cast down! I, too, am in this cell, far more weak a man than you, and Giant Despair dealt his blows at me as well as you, and keeps me from food and light. Let us both (if but to shun the shame) bear up as well as we can."

When night came on, the wife of Giant Despair said to him, "Well, will the two men yield?"

To which he said, "No, they choose to stand firm, and will not put an end to their lives."

Then said Mrs. Diffidence: "At dawn of day take them to the yard, and show them the graves where all those whom you have put to death have been thrown, and make use of threats this time."

So Giant Despair took them to this place, and said, "In ten days' time you shall be thrown in here if you do not yield. Go; get you down to your den once more." With that he beat them all the way back, and there they lay the whole day in a sad plight.

Now, when night was come, Mrs. Diffidence said to Giant Despair, "I fear much that these men live on in hopes to pick the lock of the cell and get free."

"Dost thou say so, my dear?" quoth Giant Despair to his wife; "then at sunrise I will search them."

Now on that night, as Christian and Hopeful lay in the den, they fell on their knees to pray, and knelt till the day broke; when Christian gave a start, and said, "Fool that I am, thus to lie in this dark den when I might walk at large! I have a key in my pouch, the name of which is Promise, that, I feel sure, will turn the lock of all the doors in Doubting Castle."

Then said Hopeful: "That is good news; pluck it from thy

breast and let us try it."

So Christian put it in the lock, when the bolt sprang back, the door flew wide, and Christian and Hopeful both came out. When they got to the yard door the key did just as well; but the lock of the last strong gate of Doubting Castle went hard. Yet it did turn at last, though the hinge gave so loud a creak that it woke up Giant Despair, who rose to seek for the two men. But just then he felt his limbs fail, for a fit came on him, so that he could by no means reach their cell. Christian and Hopeful now fled back to the high way, and were safe out of his grounds. When they sat down to rest on a stile, they said they would warn those who might chance to come on this road. So they cut these words on a post: "This is the way to Doubting Castle which is kept by Giant Despair, who loves not the King of the Celestial Country, and seeks to kill all who would go there."

Then they came to The Delectable Mountains, which the Lord of the Hill owns. Here they saw fruit trees, vines, shrubs, woods, and streams, and drank and ate of the grapes. Now there were men at the tops of these hills who kept watch on their flocks, and as they stood by the high way, Christian and

Hopeful leant on their staves to rest, while thus they spoke to the men: "Who owns these Delectable Mountains, and whose are the sheep that feed on them?"

Men: "These hills are Immanuel's, and the sheep are His, too, and He laid down his life for them."

Christian: "Is this the way to The Celestial City?"

Men: "You are in the right road."

Christian: "How far is it?"

Men: "Too far for all but those that shall get there, in good truth."

Christian: "Is the way safe?"

Men: "Safe for those for whom it is to be safe; but the men of sin shall fall there."

Christian: "Is there a place of rest here for those that faint on the road?"

Men: "The Lord of these Hills gave us a charge to help those that came here, should they be known to us or not; so the good things of the place are yours."

I then saw in my dream that the men said, "Whence come you, and by what means have you got so far? For but few of those that set out to come here, show their face on these hills."

So when Christian and Hopeful told their tale, the men cast a kind glance at them, and said, "With joy we greet you on The Delectable Mountains!"

Their names were Knowledge, Experience, Watchful and Sincere, and they led Christian and Hopeful by the hand to their tents, and bade them eat of that which was there, and they soon went to their rest for the night.

When the morn broke, the men woke up Christian and

Hopeful, and took them to a spot whence they saw a bright view on all sides. Then they went with them to the top of a high hill, the name of which was Error; it was steep on the far off side, and they bade them look down to the foot of it. So Christian and Hopeful cast their eyes down, and saw there some men who had lost their lives by a fall from the top; men who had been made to err, for they had put their trust in false guides.

"Have you not heard of them?" said the men.

Christian: "Yes, I have."

Men: "These are they, and to this day they have not been put in a tomb, but are left here to warn men to take good heed how they come too near the brink of this hill."

Then I saw that they had led them to the top of Mount Caution, and bade them look far off. "From that stile," said they, "there goes a path to Doubting Castle, which is kept by Giant Despair, and the men whom you see there came as you do now, till they got to that stile; and, as the right way was rough to walk in, they chose to go through a field, and there Giant Despair took them, and shut them up in Doubting Castle, where they were kept in a den for a while, till he at last sent them out quite blind, and there they are still." At this Christian gave a look at Hopeful, and they both burst out with sobs and tears, but yet said not a word.

Then the four men took them up a high hill, the name of which was Clear, that they might see the gates of The Celestial City, with the aid of a glass to look through, but their hands shook, so they could not see well.

When Christian and Hopeful thought they would move on, one of the men gave them a note of the way, and the next (Experience by name) bade them take heed that they slept not on The Enchanted Ground, and the fourth bade them God speed. Now it was that I woke from my dream.

Then I slept, and dreamt once more, and saw Christian and Hopeful go down near the foot of these hills, where lies the land of Conceit, which joins the way to Mount Zion, by a small lane. Here they met a brisk lad, whose name was Ignorance, to whom Christian said: "Whence come you, and to what place do you go?"

Ignorance, "Sir, I was born in the land that lies off there on the left, and I wish to go to The Celestial City."

Christian: "How do you think to get in at the gate?"

Ignorance: "Just as the rest of the world does."

Christian: "But what have you to show at that gate to pass you through it?"

Ignorance: "I know my Lord's will, and I have led a good life; I pay for all that I have; I give tithes, and give alms, and have left my own land for that to which I now go."

Christian: "But you came not in at the gate that is at the head of this way; you came in through a small lane; so that I fear, though you may think well of all you have done, that when the time shall come, you will have this laid to your charge, that you are a thief—and so you will not get in."

Ignorance: "Well, I know you not; do you keep to your own creed, and I will keep to mine, and I hope all will be well. And as for the gate that you talk of, all the world knows that it is far from our land, and I do not think that there is a man in all our parts who does so much as know the way to it, and I see not what need there is that he should, since we have, as you see, a fine green lane at the next turn that comes down from our part of the world."

Christian said in a low tone of voice to Hopeful, "There is more hope of a fool than of him."

Hopeful: "Let us pass on if you will, and talk to him by and by, when, may be, he can bear it."

So they went on, and Ignorance trod in their steps a short way from them, till they saw a road branch off from the one they were in, and they knew not which of the two to take.

As they stood to think of it, a man whose skin was black, but who was clad in a white robe, came to them and said,

"Why do you stand here?" They told him that they were on their way to The Celestial City, but knew not which of the two roads to take.

"Come with me, then," said the man, "for it is there that I mean to go."

So they went with him, though it was clear that the road must have made a bend, for they found they would soon turn their backs on The Celestial City.

Ere long, Christian and Hopeful were both caught in a net, and knew not what to do; and with that the white robe fell off the black man's back. Then they saw where they were. So there they sat down and wept.

Christian: "Did not one of the four men who kept guard on their sheep tell us to take heed lest Flatterer should spread a net for our feet?"

Hopeful: "Those men, too, gave us a note of the way, but we have not read it, and so have not kept in the right path." Thus they lay in the net to weep and wail.

At last they saw a Bright One come up to them with a whip of fine cord in his hand, who said: "What do you here? Whence come you?"

They told him that their wish was to go to Zion, but that they had been led out of the way by a black man with a white cloak on, who, as he was bound for the same place, said he would show them the road.

Then said he: "It is Flatterer, a false man, who has put on the garb of a Bright One for a time."

So he rent the net and let the men out. Then he bade them come with him, that he might set them in the right way once more. He said, "Where were you last night?"

Quoth they: "With the men who kept watch on their sheep on The Delectable Mountains."

Then he said, "But when you were at a stand why did you not read your note?"

They told him that they had not thought of it.

Now I saw in my dream that he bade them lie down, and whipt them sore, to teach them the good way in which they should walk; and he said, "Those whom I love I serve thus."

So they gave him thanks for what he had taught them, and went on the right way up the hill with a song of joy.

At length they came to a land the air of which made men sleep and here the lids of Hopeful's eyes dropt, and he said, "Let us lie down here and take a nap."

Christian: "By no means, lest if we sleep we wake no more."

Hopeful: "Nay, friend Christian, sleep is sweet to the man who has spent the day in toil."

Christian: "Do you not call to mind that one of the men who kept watch on the sheep bade us to take care of The Enchanted Ground? He meant by that we should take heed not to sleep; so let us not sleep; but watch."

Hopeful: "I see I am in fault."

Christian: "Now then, to keep sleep from our eyes I will ask you, as we go, to tell me how you came at first to do as you do now?"

Hopeful: "Do you mean how came I first to look to the good of my soul?"

Christian: "Yes."

Hopeful: "For a long time the things that were seen and sold at Vanity Fair were a great joy to me."

Christian: "What goods do you speak of?"

Hopeful: "All the goods of this life; such as lies, oaths, drink; in a word, love of self and all that tends to kill the soul. But I heard from you and Faithful that the end of these things is Death."

Thus did they talk as they went on their way.

But I saw in my dream that by this time Christian and Hopeful had got through The Enchanted Ground, and had come to the land of Beulah, where the air is sweet; and as their way lay through this land, they made no haste to quit it, for here they heard the birds sing all day long, and the sun shone day and night; the Valley of Death was on the left, and it was out of the reach of Giant Despair; nor could they from this place so much as see Doubting Castle.

Now were they in sight of Zion, and here some of the Bright Ones came to meet them. Here, too, they heard the voice of those who dwelt in Zion, and had a good view of this land of bliss, which was built of rare gems of all hues, and the streets were laid with gold. So that the rays of light which shone on

Land of Beulah

Christian were too bright for him to bear and he fell sick, and Hopeful had a fit of the same kind. So they lay by for a time and wept, for their joy was too much for them.

At length, step by step, they drew near to Zion, and saw that the gates were flung back.

A man stood in the way, to whom Christian and Hopeful said: "Whose vines and crops are these?"

He told them they were the King's, and were put there to give joy to those who should go on the road. So he bade them eat what fruit they chose, and took them to see the King's walks, where they slept.

Now I saw in my dream that they spoke more in their sleep than they had done all the rest of the way, and I could but muse at this. But the man said, "Why do you muse at it? The juice of this vine is so sweet as to cause the lips of them that sleep to speak."

I then saw that when they woke, they would fain go up to Zion; but as I said, the sun threw off such bright rays from The Celestial City, which was built of pure gold, that they could not, as yet, look on it, save through a glass made for that end.

Now as they went, they met with two men in white robes, and the face of each shone bright as the light. These men said, "Whence come you?" And when they had been told they said, "You have but one thing more to do, which is a hard one, and then you are in Zion."

Christian and Hopeful did then beg of the two men to go with them; which they did. "But," said they, "it is by your own faith that you must gain it."

Now 'twixt them and the gate was a fierce stream which was broad and deep. It had no bridge, and the mere sight of it did so stun Christian and Hopeful that they could not move.

But the men who went with them said, "You can not come to the gate but through this stream."

"Is there no way but this one to the gate?" said poor Christian.

"Yes," quoth they, "but there have been but two men, to wit, Enoch and Elijah, who have trod that path since the world was made."

When Christian and Hopeful cast their eyes on the stream once more, they felt their hearts sink with fear, and gave a look this way and that in much dread of the waves. Yet through it lay the way to Zion. "Is the stream all of one depth?" said Christian. He was told that it was not, yet that in that there was no help, for he would find the stream more or less deep, as he had faith in the King of the place. So they set foot on the stream, but Christian gave a loud cry to his good friend Hopeful, and said, "The waves close round my head, and I sink!" Then said Hopeful, "Be of good cheer, my feet feel the bed of the stream, and it is good."

But Christian said, "Ah, Hopeful, the pains of death have got hold of me; I shall not reach the land that I long for." And with that a cloud came on his sight, so that he could not see.

Hopeful had much to do to keep Christian's head out of the stream; nay, at times he had quite sunk, and then in a while he would rise up half dead.

Yet through it lay the way to Zion

Then said Hopeful, "My friend, all this is sent to try if you will call to mind all that God has done for you, and live on Him in your heart."

At these words Hopeful saw that Christian was in deep thought; so he said to him, "Be of good cheer; Christ will make thee whole."

Then Christian broke out with a loud voice, "Oh, I see Him, and He speaks to me and says, 'When you pass through the deep streams, I will be with you.'"

And now they both got strength, and the stream was as still as a stone, so that Christian felt the bed of it with his feet, and he could walk through it. Thus they got to the right bank, where the two men in bright robes stood to wait for them, and their clothes were left in the stream.

Now you must bear in mind that Zion was on a steep hill; yet did Christian and Hopeful go up with ease and great speed, for they had these two men to lead them by the arms.

The hill stood in the sky, for the base of it was there. So in sweet talk they went up through the air. The Bright Ones told them of the bliss of the place, which they said was such as no tongue could tell, and that there they would see the Tree of Life, and eat of the fruits of it.

"When you come there," said they, "white robes will be put on you, and your talk from day to day shall be with the King for all time. There you shall not see such things as you saw on earth, to wit: care and want, and woe and death. You now go to be with Abraham, Isaac, and Jacob."

Christian and Hopeful: "What must we do there?"

They said: "You will have rest for all your grief. You will

reap what you have sown—the fruit of all the tears you shed for the King by the way. In that place you will wear crowns of gold, and have at all times a sight of Him who sits on the Throne. There you shall serve Him with love, with shouts of joy and with songs of praise."

Now while they thus drew up to the gate, lo, a host of saints came to meet them, to whom the two Bright Ones said: "These are men who felt love for our Lord when they were in the world, and left all for His name; and He sent us to bring them far on their way, that they might go in and look on their Lord with joy."

Then the whole host with great shouts came round on all sides (as it were to guard them); so that it would seem to Christian and Hopeful as if all Zion had come down to meet them.

Now, when Christian and Hopeful went in at the gate a great change took place in them, and they were clad in robes that shone like gold. There were bright hosts that came with harps and crowns, and they said to them: "Come ye, in the joy of the Lord." And then I heard all the bells in Zion ring.

Now, just as the gates were flung back for the men to pass in, I had a sight of Zion, which shone like the sun; the ground was of gold, and those who dwelt there had love in their looks, crowns on their heads, and palms in their hands, and with one voice they sent forth shouts of praise.

But the gates were now once more shut, and I could but wish that I, too, had gone in to share this bliss. Then I woke, and, lo, it was a dream.

PART TWO

Once more I had a dream, and it was this: Christiana, the wife of Christian, had been on her knees to pray, and as she rose, she heard a loud knock at the door. "If you come in God's name," said she, "come in."

Then I thought in my dream that a form, clad in robes as white as snow, threw back the door, and said, "Peace be to this house."

At a sight so new to her, Christiana at first grew pale with fear, but in a short time took heart and told him she would fain know whence he came, and why. So he said his name was Secret, and that he dwelt with those that are on high. Then said her guest: "Christiana, here is a note for thee, which I have brought from Christian."

So she took it, broke the seal, and read these words, which were in gold: "To her who was my dear wife. The King would have you do as I have done, for that was the way to come to this land, and to dwell with Him in joy."

When Christiana read this, she shed tears, and said to him who brought the note, "Sir, will you take me and my sons with you, that we, too, may bow down to this king?"

But he said, "Christiana, joy is born of grief; care must come first, then bliss. To reach the land where I dwell, thou must go through toils, as well as scorn and taunts. But take the road that leads up to the field gate which stands in the head of the way; and I wish you all good speed. I would have thee wear this note in thy breast, that it may be read by thee till thou must give it up at the last gate that leads to The Celestial City."

Then Christiana spoke to her boys, and said, "My sons, I have of late been sad at the death of Christian, your dear sire. But I feel sure now that it is well with him, and that he dwells in the land of life and peace. I have, too, felt deep grief at the thoughts of my own state and yours; for we were wrong to let our hearts grow cold, and turn a deaf ear to him in the time of his woe, and hold back from him when he fled from this City of Destruction.

"The thought of these things would kill me, were it not for a dream which I had last night, and for what a guest who came here at dawn has told me. So come, my dear ones, let us make our way at once to the gate that leads to The Celestial City, that we may see your sire and be there with him and his friends."

Then her first two sons burst out in tears of joy that Christiana's heart was set that way.

Now while they put all things right to go, two friends of Christiana's came up to her house, and gave a knock at the door. To them she said, "If you come in God's name, come in."

This mode of speech from the lips of Christiana struck them as strange. Yet they came in, and said, "Pray what do you mean by this?"

"I mean to leave my home," said she to Mrs. Timorous — for that was the name of one of these friends.

Mrs. Timorous: "To what end, pray tell me?"

Christiana: "To go to my dear Christian." And with that she wept.

Mrs. Timorous: "Nay, can it be so? Who or what has brought you to this state of mind?"

Christiana: "Oh, my friend, if you did but know as much as I do, I doubt not that you would be glad to go with me."

Mrs. Timorous: "Pray what new lore have you got hold of that draws your mind from your friends, and tempts you to go no one knows where?"

Christiana: "I dreamt last night that I saw Christian. Oh, that my soul were with him now! The Prince of the place has sent for me, through one who came to me at sun rise, and brought this note to bid me go there; read it, I pray you."

Mrs. Timorous: "Ah, how mad to run such risks! You have heard, I am sure, from our friend Obstinate, what Christian met with on the way, for he went with him; yea, and Pliable, too, till they, like wise men, came back through fear. You heard how he met with the beasts of prey and Apollyon, what he saw in the Valley of the Shadow of Death, and more still that makes my hair stand on end to hear of; think, too, of these four sweet boys who are your own flesh and bone; and, though you should be so rash as to wish to go, yet for their sake, I pray you keep at home."

But Christiana said, "Tempt me not. I have now a chance put in my hand to get gain, and in truth I should be a fool if I had not the heart to grasp it. And these toils and snares that you tell me of shall not keep me back; no, they serve but to show me that I am in the right. Care must first be felt, then joy. So since you came not to my house in God's name, as I said, I pray you to be gone, and tempt me no more."

Then Mrs. Timorous said to Mercy (who had come with her): "Let us leave her in her own hands, since she scorns all that I say."

But Mercy thought that if her friend Christiana must be gone, she would go part of the way with her to help her. She took some thought, too, of her own soul, for what Christiana had said had laid hold on her mind, and she felt she must have some talk with this friend; and if she found that truth and life were in her words, she would join her with all her heart.

So Mercy said to Mrs. Timorous: "I came with you to see Christiana, and since on this day she takes leave of the town,

I think the least I can do would be to walk a short way with
her to help her on." But the rest she kept from Mrs. Timorous.

Mrs. Timorous: "Well, I see you have a mind to play the
fool, too; but take heed in good time, and be wise."

So Mrs. Timorous went to her own house; and Christiana,
with her four boys and Mercy, went on their way.

"Mercy," said Christiana, "I take this as a great boon that
you should set foot out of doors to start me on my way."

Then said young Mercy (for she was quite young): "If I
thought it would be good to join you, I would not go back at
all to the town."

Christiana: "Well, Mercy, cast your lot in with mine; I
know what will be the end of our toils. Christian is where he
would not fail to be for all the gold in the mines of Spain. Nor
shall you be sent back, though there be no one but I to ask it
for you; for the King who has sent for me and my boys is One
who turns not from those who seek Him. If you like I will hire
you, and you shall go as my maid, and yet shall share all
things with me, so that you do but go."

Mercy: "But how do I know that I shall be let in? If I thought I should have help from Him from whom all help comes, I would make no pause, but would go at once, let the way be as rough as it might."

Christiana: "Well, Mercy, I will tell you what I would have you do. Go with me as far as to the field gate, and there I will ask; and if no hopes should be held out to you by Him who keeps the gate, you can but go back to your home."

Mercy: "Well, I will go with you, and the Lord grant that my lot may be cast to dwell in the land for which my heart yearns."

Christiana then felt glad that she had a friend to join her, and that her friend should have so great a care for her soul.

So they went on their way; but the face of Mercy wore so sad a mien that Christiana said to her, "What ails you? Why do you weep?"

Mercy: "Oh, who could but weep to think of the state of my poor friends near and dear to me, in our bad town?"

Christiana: "You feel for your friends as my good Christian did for me when he left me, for it went to his heart to find that I would not see these things in the same light as he did. And now, you, I, and these dear boys, reap the fruits of all his woes. I hope, Mercy, these tears of yours will not be shed in vain, for He who could not lie, has said that they who sow in tears shall reap in joy."

Now when Christiana came up to the Slough of Despond, she and her sons made a stand, and Christiana told them that this was the place in which her dear Christian fell. But Mercy said, "Come, let us try; all we have to do is to keep the

steps well in view." Yet Christiana made a slip or two in the mud; but at last they got through the slough, and then they heard a voice say to them: *"Blest is she who hath faith, for those things which were told her of the Lord shall come to pass."*

So now they went on once more, and Mercy said, "Had I as good grounds to hope to get in at the gate as you have, I think no Slough of Despond would keep me back."

"Well," said Christiana, "you know your sore, and I know mine, and hard toil will it be for both of us to get to the end of the way; for how can we think that they who set out on a scheme of so much bliss, should steer clear of frights and fears on their way to that bright bourn which it is their aim to reach?"

When they came to the gate, it took them some time to make out a plan of what they should say to Him who stood there; and as Mercy was not so old as her friend, she said that it must rest with Christiana to speak for all of them. So, she gave a knock, and then (like Christian) two more; but no one came.

Now they heard the fierce bark of a dog, which made them shake with fear, nor did they dare for a while to knock a third time, lest the dog should fly at them. So they were put to their wits' end to know what to do: to knock they did not dare, for fear of the dog; to go back they did not dare, lest He who kept the gate should see them as they went, and might not like it. At last they gave a knock four times as loud as the first.

Then He who stood at the gate said, "Who is there?" The dog was heard to bark no more, and the gate swung wide for them to come in.

Christiana sank on her knees, and said, "Let not our Lord be wroth that we have made this loud noise at His gate."

At this He said: "Whence come you, and what is it that you would have?"

Quoth Christiana: "We are come from the town whence Christian came, to beg to be let in at this gate, that we may go on our way to The Celestial City. I was once the wife of Christian, who now is in the land of bliss."

With that, He who kept the gate threw up His arms and said, "What! is she on her road to The Celestial City who, but a short time since, did hate the life of that place?"

Then Christiana bent her head, and said, "Yes, and so are these, my dear sons." So He took her by the hand and led her

Now they heard the fierce bark of a dog

in; and when her four sons had gone through, He shut the gate. This done, He said to a man hard by, "Sound the Horn for joy."

But now that Christiana was safe through the gate with her boys, she thought it time to speak a word for Mercy, so she said, "My Lord, I have a friend who stands at the gate, who has come here with the same trust that I did; one whose heart is sad to think that she comes, it may be, when she is not sent for; while I had word from Christian's King to come."

The time did so lag with poor Mercy while she stood to be let in, that though it was but a short space, yet through fear and doubt did it seem to her like an hour at least; and Christiana could not say more for Mercy to Him who kept the gate for the knocks, which came so fast, and were at last so loud that they made Christiana start.

Then He said, "Who is there?"

Quoth Christiana: "It is my friend."

So He threw back the gate to look out, but Mercy was in a swoon, from the fear that she should not be let in.

Then He took her by the hand and said, "Fear not; stand firm on thy feet, and tell me whence thou art come, and for what end?"

Mercy: "I do not come as my friend Christiana does, for I was not sent for by the King, and I fear I am too bold. Yet if there is grace to share, I pray Thee let me share it."

Then He took her once more by the hand and led her in, and said, "All may come in who put their trust in me, let the means be what they may that brought them here."

Then He told those that stood by to bring her some myrrh,

and in a while she got well.

Now I saw in my dream that he spoke good words to Mercy, Christiana, and her boys, so as to make glad their hearts. And He took them up to the top of the gate, where He left them for a while, and Christiana said, "Oh, my dear friend, how glad am I that we have all got in!"

Mercy: "So you may well be; but most of all have I cause for joy."

Christiana: "I thought at one time as I stood at the gate, and none came to me, that all our pains had been lost."

Mercy: "But my worst fears came when I saw Him who kept the gate grant you your wish, and take no heed of me. And this brought to my mind the two who ground at the same mill, and how I was the one who was left; and I found it hard not to cry out, 'I am lost! I am lost!'"

Christiana: "I thought you would have come in by rude force."

Mercy: "Ah me! You saw that the door was shut on me, and that a fierce hound was not far off. Who, with so faint a heart as mine, would not give loud knocks with all her might? But pray, what said my Lord at this rude noise? Was He not wroth with me?"

Christiana: "When He heard your loud thumps at the door He gave a smile; and to my mind, what you did would seem to please Him well. But it is hard to guess why He keeps such a dog. Had I known of it, I fear I should not have had the wish to come. But now we are in, we are safe; and I am glad with all my heart."

One of Christiana's boys said: "Pray ask to have a chain

· 80 ·

put on the dog, for it will bite us when we go hence."

Then He who kept the gate came down to them once more, and Mercy fell with her face to the ground, and said, "Oh, let me bless and praise the Lord with my lips!"

So He said to her, "Peace be to thee; stand up."

But she would not rise till she had heard from Him why He kept so fierce a dog in the yard. He told her He did not own the dog, but that it was shut up in the grounds of one who dwelt near. "In truth," said He, "it is kept from no good will to me or mine, but to cause those who come here to turn back from my gate by the sound of its voice. But hadst thou known more of me thou wouldst not have felt fear of a dog. The poor man who goes from door to door will, for the sake of alms, run the risk of a bite from a cur; and shall a dog keep thee from me?"

Mercy: "I spoke of what I knew not; but, Lord, I know that Thou dost all things well."

Then Christiana rose as if she would go on her way. So He fed them, and set them in the right path, as He had done to Christian. And as they went, Christiana sang a hymn: "We turn our tears to joy, and our fears to faith."

They had not gone far when they saw some fruit trees, the boughs of which hung from the top of a wall that was built around the grounds of him who kept the fierce hound, and at times those that came that way would eat them to their cost. So as they were ripe, Christiana's boys threw them down and ate some of them; though Christiana chid them for it, and said, "That fruit is not ours." But she knew not then whose it was. Still the boys would eat of it.

Now when they had gone but a bow shot from the place, they saw two men, who with bold looks came fast down the hill to meet them. With that, Christiana and her friend Mercy, drew down their veils, and so kept on their way, and the boys went on first. Then the men came up to them, but Christiana said: "Stand back, or go by in peace, as you should." Yet they took no more heed of her words than if they had been deaf.

Christiana, who did not like their looks, said, "We are in haste, and can not stay; our work is a work of life and death." With that she and the rest made a fresh move to pass, but the men would not let them. So with one voice they all set up a loud cry. Now, as they were not far from the field gate, they were heard from that place, and some of those in the lodge came out in haste to catch these bad men; when they soon leapt the wall, and got safe to the grounds where the dog was kept.

Reliever: "How was it that when you were at the gate you did not ask Him who stood there to take you on your way, and guard you from harm? Had you done so you would not have gone through these frights, for He would have been sure to grant you your wish."

Christiana: "Ah, Sir, the joy we felt when we were let in, drove from our thoughts all fears to come. And how could we think that such bad men could lurk in such a place as that? True, it would have been well for us if we had thought to ask Him; but since our Lord knew it would be for our good, how came it to pass that He did not send some one with us?"

Reliever: "You did not ask. When the want of a thing is felt, that which we wish for is worth all the more."

Christiana: "Shall we go back to my Lord and tell Him we wish we had been more wise, and ask for a guard?"

Reliever: "Go back you need not, for in no place where you go will you find a want at all."

When he had said this he took his leave, and the rest went on their way.

Mercy: "What a blank is here! I made sure we had been past all risk, and that we should see no more care."

Christiana: "Your youth may plead for you, my friend, and screen you from blame; but as for me, my fault is so much the worse in so far as I knew what would take place ere I came out of my door."

Mercy: "But how could you know this ere you set out?"

Christiana: "Why, I will tell you. One night as I lay in bed, I had a dream, in which I saw the whole scene as it took place just now.

By this time Christiana, Mercy and the four boys had come to the house of Interpreter. Now when they drew near to the door they heard the sound of Christiana's name; for the news of her flight had made a great stir; but they knew not that she stood at the door. At last she gave a knock, as she had done at the gate, when there came to the door a young maid, Innocent by name.

Innocent: "With whom would you speak in this place?"

Christiana: "As we heard that this is a place of rest for those that go by the way, we pray that we may be let in, for the day, as you see, is far spent, and we are loth to go on by night."

Innocent: "Pray what is your name, that I may tell it to my Lord?"

Christiana: "My name is Christiana; I was the wife of Christian, who some time since came by this way, and these are his four sons."

Innocent then ran in and said to those there, "Can you guess who is at the door? There are Christiana, her boys and her friend!"

So they leapt for joy, and went to tell it to their Lord, who came to the door and said, "Art thou that Christiana whom Christian left in the town of Destruction, when he set out for The Celestial City?"

Christiana: "I am she, and my heart was so hard as to

slight his woes, and leave him to make his way as he could; and these are his four sons. But I, too, am come, for I feel sure that no way is right but this."

Interpreter: "But why do you stand at the door? Come in; it was but just now that we spoke of you, for we heard that you were on your way. Come, my dear boys, come in; come, my sweet maid, come in." So he took them to the house, and bade them sit down and rest. All in the house wore a smile of joy to think that Christiana was on her way to The Celestial City, and they were glad to see the young ones walk in God's ways, and gave them a kind of clasp of the hand to show their good will. They said soft words, too, to Mercy, and bade them all be at their ease. To fill up the time till they could sup, Interpreter took them to see all those things that had been shown to Christian. This done, they were led to a room in which stood a man with a prong in his hand, who could look no way but down on the ground; and there stood one with a

crown in his hand, which he said he would give him for his prong; yet the first man did not look up, but went on to rake the straws, dust, and stocks which lay on the floor.

Then said Christiana: "I think I know what this means. It is a sketch of a man of this world, is it not, good Sir?"

Interpreter: "Thou art right, and his prong shows that his mind is of the earth, and that he thinks life in the next world is a mere song; take note that he does not so much as look up; and straws, sticks, and dust, with most, are the great things to live for."

At that Christiana and Mercy wept, and said, "Ah, yes, it is too true!"

Interpreter then took them to a room where were a hen and her chicks, and bade them look well at them for a while. So one of the chicks went to the trough to drink, and each time she drank would she lift up her head and her eyes to the sky.

"See," said he, "what this bird does, and learn of her to know whence all good comes, and to give to the Lord who dwells on high, the praise and thanks for it. Look once more, and see all the ways that the hen has with her young brood.

RL

There is her call that goes on all day long; and there is her call that comes but now and then; she has a third call to shield them with her wings; and her fourth is a loud cry, which she gives when she spies a foe. Now," said he, "set her ways by the side of your King's, and the ways of these chicks by the side of those who love to do His will, and then you will see what I mean. For He has a way to walk in with His saints. By the call that comes all day He gives nought; by a call that is rare He is sure to have some good to give; then there is a call, too, for those that would come to His wings, which He spreads out to shield them; and He has a cry to warn men from those who might hurt their souls. I choose scenes from real life, as they are not too hard for you to grasp, when I fit them to your own case; and it is the love I have for your souls that prompts me to show you these things."

Christiana: "Pray let us see some more."

Interpreter then took them to his field, which was sown with wheat and corn; but when they came to look, the ears were cut off, and there was nought but the straw left.

Interpreter: "What shall we do with the crop?"

Christiana: "Burn some, and use the rest to dress the ground with."

Interpreter: "Fruit, you see, is the thing you look for, and for want of that you cast off the whole crop. Take heed that in this you do not seal your own doom; for by fruit I mean works."

Now when they came back to the house the meal was not yet spread, so did Christiana beg of Interpreter to show or tell them some more things.

Interpreter: "So much the more strong a man's health is, so much the more prone is he to sin. The more fat the sow is, the more she loves the mire. It is not so hard to sit up a night or two, as to watch for a whole year; just as it is not so hard to start well as it is to hold out to the end. One leak will sink a ship, and one sin will kill a man's soul. If a man would live well, let him keep his last day in mind."

Now when Christiana, Mercy and the boys had all had a good night's rest, they rose with the sun, and made a move to leave; but Interpreter told them to wait a while. "For," said he, "you must go hence in due form, such is the rule of the house."

Then he told Innocent to take them to the bath, and there wash the dust from them. This done, they came forth fresh and strong, and as Interpreter said, "Fair as the moon."

Next he told those near him to bring the seal, and when it was brought he set his mark on them that they might be known in each place where they went.

Then said Interpreter: "Bring vests for them." And they were clad in robes as white as snow, so that it made each start to see the rest shine with so bright a light.

Interpreter then sent for one of his men whose name was Great-heart, and bade that he should be clad in a coat of mail, with sword and shield, and that he should take them to a house, the name of which was Beautiful, where they would rest.

Then Interpreter took his leave of them, with a good wish for each. So they went on their way, and thus they sang:

"O move me, Lord, to watch and pray,
From sin my heart to clear;
To take my cross up day by day,
And serve the Lord with fear."

They next came to the place where Christian's load had been lost in the tomb. Here they made a pause, and gave thanks to Him who laid down His life to save theirs. So now they went up the hill, which was so steep that the toil made Christiana pant for breath.

"How can we doubt," said she, "that they who love rest more than their souls would choose some way on which they could go with more ease than this?"

Then Mercy said, "Come what may, I must rest for a while."

And James, who was the least of the boys, gave way to tears.

"Come, Come!" said Great-heart, "sit not down here; for there is a seat near us put there by the Prince." With this he took the young child by the hand, and led him to it; and they were all glad to sit down, and to be out of the heat of the sun's rays.

Then said Mercy: "How sweet is rest to them that work! And how good is the Prince to place this seat here that such as we may rest! Of this spot I have heard much, but let us take heed that we sleep not, for that once cost poor Christian dear."

Then said Mr. Great-heart: "Well, my brave boys, how do you do? What think you of this hill?"

"Sir," said James, "this hill beats me out of heart! And I see now that what I have been told is true; the land of bliss is up steps; but still, Sir, it is worse to go down hill to death than up hill to life."

"You are a good boy," said Great-heart.

At this Mercy could but smile, and it made James blush.

Christiana: "Come, will you not drink of this flask, and eat some fruit, while we sit here to rest? For Mr. Interpreter put these in my hand as I came out of his door."

Now when they had sat there a while, their guide said to

them: "The day runs on, and if you think well of it, let us now go on our way."

So they all set out, the boys first, then the rest; but they had not gone far when Christiana found she had left the flask, so she sent James back to fetch it.

Mercy: "I think this is the place where Christian lost his scroll. How was this, Sir?"

Great-heart: "We may trace it to two things; one is sleep, and one is that you cease to think of that which you cease to want; and when you lose sight of a boon you lose sight of Him who grants it, and the joy of it will end in tears."

By and by they came to a small mound with a post on it, where these words were cut, "Let him who sees this post take heed of his heart and his tongue that they be not false." Then they went on till they came up to two large beasts of prey.

Now Great-heart was a strong man, so he had no fear; but their fierce looks made the boys start, and they all clung round Great-heart.

"How now, my boys! You march on first, as brave as can be, when there is no cause for fear; but when a test of your strength comes, you shrink."

Now when Great-heart drew his sword to force a way, there came up one Giant Grim, who said in a gruff voice, "What right have you to come here?"

Great-heart: "These folk are on their way to The Celestial City, and this is the road they shall go, in spite of thee and the wild beasts."

Grim: "This is not their way, nor shall they go on it. I am

come forth to stop them, and to that end will back the wild beasts."

Now, to say the truth, so fierce were these beasts, and so grim the looks of them that the road was grown with weeds and grass from want of use. And still Grim bade them turn, "For," said he, "you shall not pass."

But their guide came up, and struck so hard at him with his sword as to force him to fall back.

Giant Grim: "Will you slay me on my own ground?"

Great-heart: "It is the King's high way on which we stand, and in His way it is that you have put these beasts. But these, who are in my charge, though weak, shall hold on in spite of all." And with that he dealt him a blow that brought him to the ground; so Giant Grim was slain.

Then Great-heart said, "Come now with me, and you shall take no harm from the two beasts." So they went by, but shook from head to foot at the mere sight of their teeth and claws.

At length they came in sight of the lodge, to which they soon went up, but made the more haste to get there as it grew dusk. So when they were come to the gate the guide gave a knock, and the man at the lodge said in a loud voice, "Who is there?"

Great-heart: "It is I."

Mr. Watchful: "How now, Mr. Great-heart? What has brought you here at so late an hour?" Then Great-heart told him that he had come with some friends on their way to Zion.

Mr. Watchful: "Will you go in and stay till day?"

Great-heart: "No, I will go back to my Lord this night."

And still Grim bade them turn

Christiana: "Ah, Sir, I know not how we can part with you, for it is to your stout heart that we owe our lives. You have fought for us, you have taught us what is right, and your faith and your love have known no bounds."

Mercy: "O that we could have you for our guide all the rest of the way! For how can such weak folk as we are hold out in a path fraught with toils and snares, if we have no friends to take us?"

James: "Pray, Sir, keep with us and help us, when the way we go is so hard to find."

Great-heart: "As my Lord wills, so must I do; if He send me to join you once more, I shall be glad to wait on you. But it was here that you were in fault at first, for when He bade me come thus far with you, if you had said, "We beg of you to let him go quite through with us," He would have let me do so. But now I must go back; and so good Christiana, Mercy and my dear boys, fare ye all well."

Then did Watchful, who kept the lodge, ask Christiana whence she had come and who her friends were.

Christiana: "I come from The City of Destruction, and I was the wife of one Christian, who is dead."

Then Watchful rang the bell, as at such times he is wont, and there came to the door a maid, to whom he said: "Go, make it known that Christiana, the wife of Christian, and her four boys are come on their way to The Celestial City."

So she went in and told all this. And, oh, what shouts of joy were sent forth when those words fell from her mouth! So all came with haste to Watchful; for Christiana still stood at the door.

Some of the most grave said to her, "Christiana, come in, thou wife of that good man, come in, thou blest one, come in, with all that are with thee."

So she went in, and the rest with her. They then bade them sit down in a large room, where the chief of the house came to see them and to cheer his guests. Then he gave each of them a kiss. But as it was late, and Christiana and the rest were faint with the great fright they had had, they would fain have gone to rest.

"Nay," said those of the house, "take first some meat; for as Watchful had heard that they were on their way, a lamb had been slain for them." When the meal had come to an end, and they had sung a psalm, Christiana said, "If we may be so bold as to choose, let us be in that room which was Christian's when he was here."

So they took them there, but ere she went to sleep, Christiana said, "I did not think when my poor Christian set off with his load on his back that I should do the same thing."

Mercy: "No, nor did you think then that you should rest in the same room as he had done."

Christiana: "And less still to see his dear face once more who was dead and gone, and to praise the Lord the King with him; and yet now I think I shall."

Mercy: "Do you not hear a noise?"

Christiana: "Hark! as far as I can make out, the sounds we hear come from the lute, the pipe, and the horn."

Mercy: "Sweet sounds in the house, sweet sounds in the air, sweet sounds in the heart, for joy that we are here."

Thus did Christiana and Mercy chat, and they then slept.

Now at dawn when they woke up, Christiana said to Mercy: "What was it that made you laugh in your sleep last night? Were you in a dream?"

Mercy: "Yes, and a sweet dream it was. But are you sure that I did laugh?"

Christiana: "Yes, you gave a laugh as if from your heart of hearts. Do pray, Mercy, tell it to me."

Mercy: "I dreamt that I lay in some lone wood to weep and wail, for that my heart should be so hard a one. Now I had not been there long when I thought there were some who had come to hear me speak in my sleep; but I went on with my moans. At this they said with a laugh that I was a fool. Then I saw a Bright One with wings come up to me, who said, 'Mercy, what ails you?' And when he heard the cause of my grief, he said, 'Peace be to thee.' He then came up to wipe off my tears and had me clad in robes of gold, and put a chain on my neck, and a crown on my head. Then he took me by the hand and said, 'Mercy, come this way.' So he went up with me till we came to a gate, at which he gave a knock and then he took me to a throne on which one sat. The place was as bright as the stars, nay more like the sun. And I thought that I saw Christian there. So I woke from my dream. But did I laugh?"

Christiana: "Laugh! Yes, and so you might, to see how well off you were! For you must give me leave to tell you, that as you find the first part true, so you will find true the last."

Mercy: "Well, I am glad of my dream, for I hope ere long to see it come to pass, so as to make me laugh once more."

Christiana: "I think it is now high time to rise, and to know what we must do."

Mercy: "Pray, if they should ask us to stay, let us by all means do so; for I should much like to know more of these maids. I think Prudence, Piety, and Charity have, each of them, a most choice mien."

Christiana: "We shall see what they will do."

So they came down.

Then Prudence and Piety: "If you will stay, here you shall have what the house will yield."

Charity: "Yes, and that with a good will."

So they were there some time, much to their good.

Prudence: "Christiana, I give you all praise, for you have brought your boys up well. With James I have had a long chat; he is a good boy, and has learnt much that will bring peace to his mind, while he lives on this earth, and in the world to come it will cause him to see the face of Him who sits on the throne. For my own part, I will teach all your sons." At the same time, said she to them: "You must still give heed to all that Christiana can teach you, but more than all, you must read the Book of God's Word, which sent your dear sire on his way to the land of bliss."

By the time that Christiana and the rest had been in this place a week, a man, Mr. Brisk by name, came to woo Mercy, with the wish to wed her. Now Mercy was fair to look on and her mind was at all times set on work and the care of those round her. She would knit hose for the poor, and give to all those things of which they stood in need.

"She will make me a good house wife," thought Brisk.

Mercy one day said to those of the house, "Will you tell me what you think of Mr. Brisk?"

They then told her that the young man would seem to have a great sense of the love of God, but that they had fears it did not reach his soul, which they thought did cleave too much to this world.

"Nay then," said Mercy, "I will look no more on him, for I will not have a clog to my soul."

Prudence: "If you go on as you have set out, and work so hard for the poor, he will soon cool."

So the next time he came, he found her at her work.

"What, still at it?" said he.

Mercy: "Yes."

Mr. Brisk: "How much can you earn in the day."

Mercy: "I work at these things for the good of those for whom I do them; and more than this, to do the will of Him who was slain on the cross for me."

With that his face fell, and he came no more to see her.

Prudence: "Did I not tell you that Mr. Brisk would soon flee from you? Yea, he may seem to love Mercy, but Mercy and he should not tread the same road of life side by side."

Now Matthew, the son of Christiana, fell sick, so they sent to Mr. Skill to cure him. Then said he: "Tell me what he eats."

Christiana: "Well, there is no food here but what is good."

Mr. Skill: "This boy has in him a crude mass of food, which if I do not use the means to get rid of he will die."

Samuel said to Christiana, "What was it that you saw Matthew pick up and eat when we came from the gate which

is at the head of this way?"

Christiana: "It was some of the fruit that grows there; I chid him for it."

Skill: "I felt sure that it was some bad food; now that fruit hurts more than all, for it is the fruit from Beelzebub's grounds. Did no one warn you of it? Some fall down dead when they eat it."

Then Christiana wept and said, "What shall I do for my son? Pray, Sir, try your best to cure him, let it cost what it may."

Then Skill gave strange drugs to him, which he would not take. So Christiana put one of them to the tip of her tongue. "Oh, Matthew," said she, "it is sweet, sweet as balm; if you love me, if you love Mercy, if you love your life, do take it!"

So in time he did, and felt grief for his sin. He quite lost the pain, so that with a staff he could walk, and went from room to room to talk with Mercy, Prudence, Piety and Charity.

Christiana: "Pray, Sir, what else are these pills good for?"

Skill: "They are good for all those that go on their way to The Celestial City."

Christiana: "I pray of you to make me up a large box full of them, for if I can get these, I will take none else."

Skill: "I make no doubt that if a man will but use them as he should, he could not die. But good Christiana, these pills will be of no use if you do not give them as I have done, and that is, in a glass of grief for the sins of those who take them." So he gave some to Christiana and the rest of her boys, and to Mercy; he bade Matthew, too, keep a good look out that he ate no more green plums; then he gave them a kiss, and went his way.

Now, as they had spent some time here, they made a move to go. Then Joseph, who was Christiana's third son, said to her: "You were to send to the house of Mr. Interpreter to beg him to grant that Mr. Great-heart should go with us as our guide."

"Good boy!" said Christiana, "I had not thought of it."

So she wrote a note, and Interpreter said to the man who brought it, "Go, tell them that I will send him."

Great-heart soon came, and he said to Christiana and Mercy, "My Lord has sent you some wine and burnt corn, and to the boys figs and dry grapes."

They then set off, and Prudence and Piety went with them. But first Christiana took leave of Watchful, who kept the gate, and put a small coin in his hand while she gave him her thanks for all that he had done for her and her dear boys. She then said to him, "Have you seen men go by since we have been here?"

Watchful: "Yes, I have, and there has been a great theft on this high way; but the thieves were caught."

Then Christiana and Mercy said they felt great fear to go on that road.

Matthew: "Fear not, as long as we have Mr. Great-heart with us to guide us."

I now saw in my dream that they went on till they came to the brow of the hill, when Piety said, "O, I must go back to fetch that which I meant to give to Christiana and Mercy, and it was a list of all those things which they had seen at the house where we live. On these," said she, "I beg of you to look from time to time, and call them to mind for your good."

They now went down the hill to the Vale of Humiliation. It was a steep hill, and their feet slid as they went on; but they took great care, and when they had got to the foot of it, Piety said to Christiana: "This is the vale where Christian met with Apollyon and where they had that fierce fight which I know you must have heard of. But be of good cheer, as long as we have Mr. Great-heart to guide us, there is nought here that will hurt us, save those sights that spring from our own fears. And as to Apollyon, the good folk of the town, who tell us that such a thing fell out in such a place, to the hurt of such a one, think that some foul fiend haunts that place, when lo! it is from the fruit of their own ill deeds that such things do fall on them. For they that make slips must look for frights. And hence it is that this vale has so bad a name."

James: "See, there is a post with words on it, I will go and read them."

So he went, and found that these words were cut on it: "Let the slips which Christian met with ere he came here, and the fights he had in this place, warn all those who come to the Vale of Humiliation."

Mr. Great-heart: "It is not so hard to go up as down this hill, and that can be said of but few hills in this part of the world. But we will leave the good man, he is at rest, and he had a brave fight with the foe; let Him who dwells on high grant that we fare no worse when our strength comes to be put to the test. This vale brings forth much fruit."

Now, as they went on, they met a boy who was clad in mean clothes and kept watch on some sheep. He had a fine fresh face, and as he sat on the bank he sang a song.

"Hark," said Great-heart, "to the words of that boy's song."

So they gave ear to it.

"He that is down need fear no fall,
He that is low, no pride,
He that is meek at all times shall
Have God to be his guide."

Then said Great-heart: "Do you hear him? I dare say this boy leads as gay a life as he that is clad in silk, and that he wears more of that plant which they call heart's ease."

Samuel: "Ask Great-heart in what part of this vale it was that Apollyon came to fight Christian?"

Great-heart: "The fight took place at that part of the plain which has the name of Forgetful Green. And if those who go

As he sat on the bank he sang a song

on their way, meet with a shock, it is when they lose sight of the good which they have at the hand of Him who dwells on high."

Mercy: "I think I feel as well in this place as I have done in all the rest of our way. This vale has a sweet grace, and just suits my mind; for I love to be in such a spot as this, where there are no coach wheels to make a din. Here one may think a while what he is, whence he came, and for what the King has made him; here one may muse and pray."

Just then they thought that the ground they trod on shook. But the guide bade them be of good cheer, and look well to their feet, lest by chance they should meet with some snare.

Then James felt sick, but I think the cause of it was fear, and Christiana gave him some of the wine which Mr. Interpreter had put in her hands, and three of the pills which Mr. Skill had made up, and the boy soon got well.

They then went on a while, and Christiana said, "What is that thing on the road? A thing of such a shape I have not seen in all my life!"

Joseph said, "What is it?"

"A vile thing, child, a vile thing!" said she.

Joseph: "But what is it like?"

Christiana: "It is like — I can't tell what. Just then it was far off, now it is nigh."

Great-heart: "Well, let them that have the most fear keep close to me."

Then it went out of sight of all of them.

But they had not gone far when Mercy cast a look back, and saw a great beast come fast up to them with a loud roar.

This noise made them all quail with fright save their guide, who fell back and put the rest in front of him. But when the brute saw that Great-heart meant to fight him, he drew back and was seen no more.

Now they had not left the spot long when a great mist fell on them, so that they could not see.

"What shall we do?" said they.

Their guide told them not to fear, but to stand still, and see what an end he would put to this too.

Then said Christiana to Mercy: "Now I see what my poor dear Christian went through; I have heard much of this place. Poor man, he went here in the dead of the night, and no one with him; but who can tell what the Valley of the Shadow of Death should mean, till they come to see it? To be here fills my breast with awe!"

Great-heart: "It seems now as if the earth and its bars were round us. I would not boast, but I trust we shall still make our way. Come, let us pray for light to Him that can give it."

So did they weep and pray. And as the path was now more smooth, they went straight on.

Mercy: "To be here is not so sweet as it was at The Gate, or at Mr. Interpreter's, or at the good house where we were last."

"Oh," said one of the boys, "it is not so bad to go through this place as it is to dwell here for all time; for aught I know we have to go this way that our last home may seem to us the more blest."

Great-heart: "Well said, Samuel; thou dost now speak like a man."

Samuel: "Why, if I do in truth get out of this place, I think I shall prize that which is light and good more than I have done all my life."

Great-heart: "We shall be out by and by."

So on they went.

Joseph: "Can we not see to the end of this vale yet?"

Great-heart: "Look to your feet, for you will soon be where the snares are."

So they took good heed.

Great-heart: "Men come here and bring no guide with them; hence it is they die from the snares they meet with in the way. Poor Christian! it is strange he should have got out of this place, and been safe. But God dwelt in his soul, and he had a stout heart, of his own, or else he could not have done it."

Christiana: "I wish that there were some inn here where we could all take rest."

"Well," said Mr. Honest — one whom they had just met — "there is such a place not far off."

So there they went, and the host, whose name was Gaius, said, "Come in, for my house was built for none but such as you."

Great-heart: "Good Gaius, let us sup. What have you for us to eat? We have gone through great toils, and stand much in want of food."

Gaius: "It is too late for us to go out and seek food; but of such as we have you shall eat."

The meal was then spread, and near the end of the feast all sat round the board to crack nuts, when old Honest said to Gaius, "Tell me what this verse means:

> '*A man there was, and some did count him mad;*
> *The more that this man gave the more he had.*'"

Then all the youths gave a guess as to what Gaius would say to it; so he sat still a while, and then said:

> "*He that gives his goods to the poor,*
> *Shall have as much and ten times more.*"

Joseph: "I did not think, Sir, that you would have found it out."

Gaius: "Ah! I have learnt of my Lord to be kind, and I find I gain by it."

Then Samuel said in a low tone to Christiana, "This is a good man's house; let us make a long stay, and why should not Matthew wed Mercy here?"

When Gaius heard him say this, quoth he: "With all my heart." And he gave Mercy to Matthew to wife.

In course of time Christiana's son James had come of age, and Gaius gave Phebe (who was his child) to be his wife. They spent ten days at the house of Gaius, and then took their leave. But on the last day he made them a feast, of which they all ate and drank.

Great-heart: "Now, Gaius, the hour has come that we must be gone; so tell me what I owe you for this long stay at your inn, for we have been here some years."

Gaius: "At my house no one pays; for the good Samaritan

told me that I was to look to him for all the cost I was put to."

They now took leave of him and went on their way, when they met with all kinds of frights and fears, till they came to a place which bore the name of Vanity Fair. There they went to the house of Mr. Mnason, who said to his guests: "If there be a thing that you stand in need of, do but say so, and we will do what we can to get it for you."

"Well, then," said they, "we should like much to see some of the good folk in this town."

So Mnason gave a stamp with his foot, at which Grace came up, and he sent her to fetch some of his friends who were in the house, and they all sat down to a meal.

Then said Mr. Mnason, as he held out his hand to point to Christiana: "My friends, I have guests here who are on their way to Zion. But who do you think this is? This is the wife of Christian whom (with his friend Faithful) the men of this town did treat so ill."

"Well," said they, "who would have thought to meet Christiana at this place! May The King whom you love and serve bring you where He is, in peace!"

They then told her that the blood of Faithful had lain like a load on their hearts; and that since they had burnt him no more men had been sent to the Stake at Vanity Fair. "In those days," said they, "good men could not walk the streets, but now they can show their heads."

Christiana and her sons and Mercy made this place their home for some years, and in course of time Mr. Mnason, who had a wife and two girls, gave his first born, whose name was Grace, to Samuel to wife, and Martha to Joseph.

Now, one day, a huge snake came out of the woods and slew some of the folk of the town. None of these were so bold as to dare to face him, but all fled when they heard that he came near, for he took off the babes by scores.

But Great-heart and the rest of the men who were at Mr. Mnason's house, made up their minds to kill this snake, and so rid the town of him. So they went forth to meet him, and at first the snake did not seem to heed them; but as they were strong men at arms, they drove him back. Then they lay in wait for him, and fell on him, till at last they knew he must die of his wounds. By this deed Mr. Great-heart and the rest won the good will of the whole town.

The time now drew near for them to go on their way. Mr. Great-heart went first as their guide; and I saw in my dream that they came to the stream on this side of The Delectable Mountains, where fine trees grew on each bank, the leaves of which were good for the health, and the fields were green all the year round; and here they might lie down and be safe. Here, too, there were folds for sheep, and a house was built in which to rear the lambs, and there was One who kept watch on them, who would take them in His arms and lay them in His breast.

Now Christiana bade the four young wives place their babes by the side of this stream, so that they might lack nought in time to come. "For," said she, "if they should stray or be lost, He will bring them back; He will give strength to the sick, and here they shall not want meat, drink, or clothes." So they left their young ones to Him.

When they went to By-Path Meadow they sat on the stile

So they went forth to meet him

to which Christian had gone with Hopeful, when Giant Despair shut the two up in Doubting Castle. They sat down to think what would be the best thing to do, now that they were so strong a force, and had such a man as Mr. Great-heart to guide them; to wit, if it would not be well to pull down Doubting Castle, and should there be poor souls shut up there who were on their way to The Celestial City, to set them free. One said this thing and one said that; at last quoth Mr. Great-heart: "We are told in the book of God's Word, that we are to fight the good fight. And, I pray, with whom should we fight if not with Giant Despair? So who will go with me?"

Christiana's four sons said, "We will"; for they were young and strong; so they left their wives and went.

When they gave their knock at the gate, Giant Despair and his wife Diffidence, came to them.

Giant Despair: "Who and what is he that is so bold as to come to the gate of Giant Despair?"

Great-heart: "It is I, a guide to those who are on their way to Zion. And I charge thee to throw wide thy gates and stand forth, for I am come to slay thee and pull down thy house."

Giant Despair: "What, shall such as Great-heart make me fear? No!"

So he put a cap of steel on his head, and with a breast plate of fire, and a club in his hand, he came out to fight his foes.

Then these six men made up to him, and they fought for their lives, till Despair was brought to the ground and put to death by Great-heart. Next they fell on his house, but it

took six days to pull it down. They found there Mr. Despond-
ency and one Much-afraid, his child, and set them free.

Then they all went on to The Delectable Mountains. They
made friends with the men that kept watch on their flocks,
who were as kind to them as they had been to Christian and
Hopeful.

"You have brought a good train with you," said they.
"Pray, where did you find them?"

So their guide told them how it had come to pass.

· 116 ·

By and by they got to The Enchanted Ground, where the air makes men sleep. Now they had not gone far, when a thick mist fell on them so that for a while they could not see; and as they could not walk by sight, they kept near their guide by the help of words. But one fell in a bush, while one stuck fast in the mud, and some of the young ones lost their shoes in the mire. "Oh, I am down!" said one. "Where are you?" cried the next; while a third said, "I am held fast in the bush!"

Then they came to a bench, Slothful's Friend by name, which had shrubs and plants round it, to screen those who sat there from the sun. But Christiana and the rest gave such good heed to what their guide told them, that though they were worn out with toil, yet there was not one of them that had so much as a wish to stop there; for they knew that it would be death to sleep but for a short time on The Enchanted Ground.

Now as it was still dark, their guide struck a light that he might look at his map (the book of God's Word); and had he not done so, they would all have been lost, for just at the end of the road was a pit, full of mud, and no one can tell how deep.

Then thought I: "Who is there but would have one of these maps or books in which he may look when he is in doubt, and knows not which way he should take?"

They soon came to a bench, on which sat two men, Heedless and Too-bold; and Christiana and the rest shook their heads for they saw that these men were in a bad case. They knew not what they ought to do; to go on and leave them

in their sleep, or to try to wake them. Now the guide spoke
to them by name; but not a sound could he hear from their
lips. So Great-heart at last shook them, and did all he could
to wake them.

One of the two, whose name was Heedless, said, "Nay, I
will pay you when I get in my debts."

At this the guide shook his head.

Then Too-bold spoke out: "I will fight as long as I can hold
my sword."

When he had said this all who stood round gave a laugh.

Christiana: "What does this mean?"

Great-heart: "They talk in their sleep. If you strike or shake
them, they will still talk in the same way, for their sleep is
like that of the man on the mast of a ship, when the waves of
the sea beat on him."

Then did Christiana, Mercy and their train go on with fear,
and they sought from their guide a light for the rest of the way.

But as the poor babes' cries were loud for want of rest, all
fell on their knees to pray for help. And, by the time that

they had gone but a short way, a wind sprang up which drove off the fog; so, now that the air was clear, they made their way.

Then they came to the land of Beulah, where the sun shines night and day. Here they took some rest, and ate of the fruit that hung from the boughs round them. But all the sleep that they could wish for in such a land as this was but for a short space of time; for the bells rang to such sweet tunes, and such a blaze of lights burst on their eyes, that they soon rose to walk to and fro on this bright way, where no base feet dare to tread.

And now they heard shouts rise up, for there was a noise in the town that a post was come from The Celestial City with words of great joy for Christiana, the wife of Christian. So search was made for her, and the house was found in which she was.

Then the post put a note in her hands, the words of which were: "Hail, good Christiana! I bring thee word that the Lord calls for thee, to stand near His throne in robes of white, in ten days' time."

When he who brought the note had read it to her, he gave her a sign that they were words of truth and love, and said he had come to bid her make haste to be gone. The sign was a shaft with a sharp point, which was to tell her, that at the time the note spoke of, she must die.

Christiana heard with joy that her toils would so soon be at an end, and that she should once more live with her dear Christian.

She then sent for her sons and their wives to come to her.

To these she gave words of good cheer. She told them how glad she was to have them near her at such a time. She sought, too, to make her own death, now close at hand, of use to them, from this time up to the hour when they should each of them have to quit this world. Her hope was that it might help guide them on their path; that the Faith which she had taught them to cling to, would have sunk deep in their hearts; and that all their works should spring from love to God. She could but pray that they would bear these words in mind, and put their whole trust in Him who had borne their sins on the Cross, and had been slain to save them.

When the day came that she must go forth to the world of love and truth, the road was full of those who would fain see her start on her way; and the last words that she was heard to say were: "I come, Lord, to be with Thee."

THE END